PROJECT MARINER

At 6:37 P.M. on August 26, 1962, the countdown began for Mariner II. At 1:43 the Atlas rocket with 360,000 pounds of thrust lifted off, and Mariner was on its way—destination Venus.

Irwin Stambler and Gordon Ashmead in this exciting account of Project Mariner give us a minute-by-minute description of the preparation, the launch, the tracking of the exploratory space vehicle. We relive the four months of waiting, the touch and go of success, the near failure of the last moment of Mariner to show the Venus-encounter sequence. And we witness the elation on December 14, when Mariner reached its closest approach to Venus.

Mars is the next target for Mariner, and the authors discuss at length what we know about Mars as well as the plans and progress of the Mariner Mars probe.

PROJECT
MARINER

By
Irwin Stambler
and
Gordon Ashmead

G. P. PUTNAM'S SONS   NEW YORK

*To the Payson Family—Stella and J.J.
and Billy, Elaine, Francis, Bob,
Sammy, Joann, Marty and Dotty*

Published simultaneously in the Dominion of
Canada by Longmans Canada Limited, Toronto.

Library of Congress Catalog Card Number: 64-
25760

MANUFACTURED IN THE UNITED STATES
OF AMERICA

10-UP

ACKNOWLEDGMENTS

We live in an age of adventure equal to any in history. A few years ago, even a small earth satellite seemed possible only in science fiction. But now men send automated space ships past Venus and Mars. Before too long man himself will make such journeys—and more besides.

There are surprisingly many people who accept all this with as much excitement as if the new achievements were just like walking around the block. But to us, the inroads on the secrets of space are truly stirring events, among the grandest moments in the saga of man. It has, then, been a privilege to discuss the behind-the-scenes operations with the scientists and engineers responsible for such programs as Project Mariner. We wish to thank the National Aeronautics and Space Agency and its Jet Propulsion Laboratory for their unstinting assistance. We appreciate both the background information provided us by these organizations and their suggestions for improving the technical accuracy of the manuscript.

In particular, we would like to thank William Schimandle, Tom Bilbo and Dan Schneiderman of the JPL technical staff in Pasadena, California, and Don Hearth of NASA Headquarters program office in Washington, D.C., for graciously discussing some of the events in the Mariner project with us. Thanks are also due to the public information officers of both NASA and JPL, including Stan Miller, June Ruggles of NASA and Frank Colella and Frank Bristow of JPL. For information on current research on the Martian environment, we are also indebted to Richard Young of NASA Ames Laboratory, Moffett Field, California.

Other organizations which have been most helpful include General Dynamics/Astronautics, Lockheed Missile and Space Div., Ryan Aeronautical Co., and North American Aviation.

PROJECT MARINER

CHAPTER 1

ARE THERE "flying saucers"? Probably not. Yet, imagine you were somehow living on the planet Venus on December 14, 1962. If you were watching some sensitive instruments scanning the heavens—say, a radar screen—something strange would suddenly occur. Across the scope, at an altitude of over 21,000 miles, a blip would appear. It would pass across the screen for about forty-two minutes, then disappear—never to return. "What was it?" you would ask. "Did I really see something go past the planet or was it just some strange but natural heavenly event?" A few years later, in 1965, the same scene might be repeated on the planet Mars.

Flying saucers coming *to* earth from outer space are unlikely, but man can probe space and the planets. That much we know. We of earth can find out about Venus and Mars. This has been proven—is continuing to be proven by Project Mariner. It was Mariner II our imaginary Venusian would have seen on his radarscope (he couldn't have seen it directly with a telescope or the naked eye because Venus is covered with a thick cloud cover).

Mariner II scored a resounding first in space for the United States. After so many heartbreaking near misses in other space goals, this country had finally achieved the honor of making the first direct observation of another planet. And the Martian event? This would have been Mariner C, the U.S. bid to follow its Venusian achievement with a similar first look at Mars.

The roots of the Mariner saga go back to the IGY (International Geophysical Year, 1957-1958). It was then that the first satellite was placed in orbit around the earth when Russia successfully launched its Sputnik I on October 4, 1957. Up to that time, the space program of the United States had been fragmented. Each of the military services had had special groups working on various aspects of military rocketry. The Army, for instance, had a group of scientists, many of them former German rocket experts, working under Dr. Wernher von Braun, in Huntsville, Alabama. The Army also supported the Jet Propulsion Laboratory of the California Institute of Technology in Pasadena, California. The Air Force had its Ballistic Missile Division in Inglewood, California, and supported such civilian research teams as Ramo-Wooldridge Corporation. The Naval Research Laboratory also performed missile research. The civilian National Advisory Committee for Aeronautics (NACA), established in 1915 by Congress to perform research work in the field of aeronautics, also was doing much important basic research in the rocket field. NACA maintained a rocket-launch facility at Wallops Island, Virginia, and supervised flights of advanced research vehicles at Edwards Air Force Base, California.

With the worldwide scientific agreement in the mid-1950's for an International Geophysical Year, the Navy was assigned the task of developing the first U.S. satellite, Project Vanguard. Actually, both the United States and Russia were latecomers to the satellite idea. The defeat of the Germans in World War II brought to light the advanced plans of German scientists at Peenemünde for a future satellite program. The Russians immediately began working to develop their own

Venus and Mars are the two primary goals of Project Mariner and its successor, Project Voyager. **Above:** The picture of Venus, taken from Earth, shows a crescent phase of the planet with the ever-present cloud cover glimmering in the sunlight.

rocket capability in secret. The United States started and stopped its own program sporadically until the early 1950's.

With Sputnik's success, it was evident that a wholesale revision of this country's approach to missiles and space research was required. In November 1957, President Eisenhower created a Scientific Advisory Committee to review the situation and recommend the future course of the nation's space effort. It was suggested that a central civilian agency be established to coordinate the work. It had to be a civilian agency to conform to the country's desires for the peaceful exploration of space.

Accordingly, on October 1, 1958, after Congress had passed the necessary laws, the National Aeronautics and Space Administration (NASA) was established. To NASA was given all the NACA facilities, the Army's Huntsville group, its Jet Propulsion Laboratory and the Navy Vanguard group. The first administrator appointed by President Eisenhower was Dr. T. Keith Glennan. In 1961, following the inauguration of President Kennedy, James E. Webb replaced Dr. Glennan as the second head of NASA.

Over the years from 1958, first slowly, then with gathering momentum, NASA established and then set into motion a vast U.S. program. It was decided that a step-by-step program of research was needed, including both manned and unmanned exploration of the solar system. The responsibility for the programs involving unmanned study of the moon and planets was given to the Jet Propulsion Laboratory (JPL) under the direction of its distinguished director, Dr. W. H. Pickering. By the fall of 1960, the Ranger program for unmanned exploration of the moon was well under way at JPL and preliminary plans were being made for the next step: the Mariner planetary-exploration program. Over-all responsibility for the Mariner program was originally assigned by NASA to Dr. Abe Silverstein's Office of Space Flight Programs and was later transferred to Dr. Homer Newell's Office of Space Sciences.

Our getting to Venus first seemed an unlikely goal in those years. The Russians were ahead in booster capability. They had proven their ability to orbit larger and larger payloads—payloads much beyond the United States' capability at the time. In September 1959, the Russians landed the first probe on the moon with Lunik II. Though little information was forthcoming about their future plans, many signs pointed to an early attempt to send the first earth probe to the planets.

CHAPTER 2

O N FEBRUARY 12, 1961, with the Mariner program hardly under way, the report came from Moscow that the first Soviet Venus probe was successfully aloft. On this day, Sputnik VIII was sent into orbit around the earth and, while orbiting, it launched an instrumented probe toward Venus. Russian scientists predicted the probe would pass within 62,500 miles of Venus on May 19 or 20.

NASA and JPL, though, were not deterred. The U.S. program was established to gain information about space. The information was just as important whether it was obtained a year before the Russians or a year after. While it is always welcome to be there first, in the long run it is the quality and quantity of data that provide the real rewards for mankind in any kind of research. Still, a first would have been nice.

Before this, it had usually been the United States which had tried first and failed. Three U.S. lunar probes had been aimed at the moon

MARS 1956

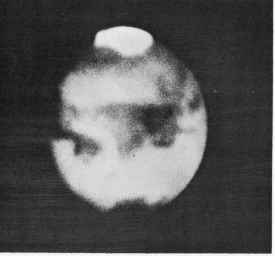 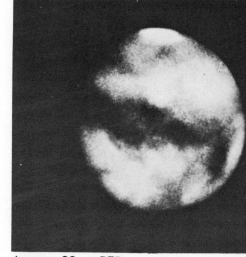

August 10　ORANGE　　　August 22　RED

These Mars photographs were taken with the 60-inch reflecting telescope at
Mt. Wilson Observatory, Calif., using different colored light filters. They are

in the years before Lunik II had succeeded. But space is a hard task-
master. Day after day, throughout February 1961, signals from the
Russian probe were beamed to earth from interplanetary space. Then,
on February 27, after the craft had traveled 4,500,000 of the 180,-
000,000 miles to Venus, something went wrong. Soviet scientists indicated they had lost contact with the probe.

Since the orbiting of the planets around the sun is elliptical, the
distances between the planets varies greatly. First the planets' orbits
bring them closer and closer to a minimum point, then the distance
increases till it reaches a maximum point, after which they move closer
together again. This fact sharply restricts the time periods in which
spacecraft can be launched to other planets.

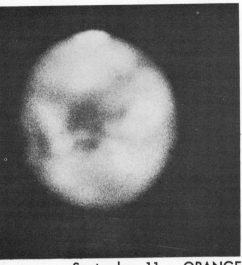
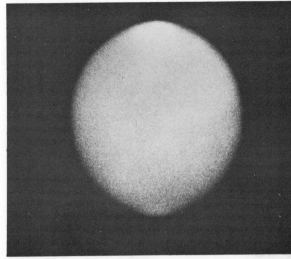

September 11   ORANGE   September 11   BLUE

from the inferior conjunction, or point of closest approach, of Mars and Earth in mid '56.

With the vast distances involved, a spaceship must be sent out when the distance traveled to reach the other planet is close to the minimum.

These favorable launch intervals are usually measured in years. For a Mars probe, such a favorable time occurred during several months of 1962. If a probe was not launched then, it would be two years before another Mars launch window was available. For Venus, the interval is usually shorter—about nineteen months. Thus the failure of the Soviet 1961 Venus probe meant they had to wait till mid-1962 if they wanted to try again. The Russians, of course, secretly did begin to prepare for another attempt the following year.

But now the U.S. Mariner program was moving along, with JPL pointing its Venus program toward the 1962 window. The plans called for the design of Mariner A during 1961, with testing of the craft to begin late in the year or at the beginning of 1962. Three flight vehicles were to be delivered to the Atlantic Missile Range, Cape Canaveral,* Florida. They were to cover two launch attempts between July and September of 1962 with the third vehicle kept in reserve in case one of the other two failed. Providing for two launches gave extra insurance, if one didn't make it, the other might. Of course, in the happy event that both attempts succeeded, the scientists would receive twice as much data.

During late 1960 and early 1961, under the direction of JPL Planetary Programs Director R. J. Parks, the many different engineering and scientific tasks were reviewed and groups were formed to handle the major design areas. Capable technical personnel had to be found either within JPL or hired from the outside to fill the available jobs. These engineers and scientists then not only had to make the basic-design decisions but they also had to line up an industry team of highly capable companies to provide engineering support and help build portions of the key equipment.

Some engineering groups were concerned with choosing the materials and designing the basic Mariner structure. Others worked on control systems to line up the craft accurately on the proper path in space. Still other physicists and mathematicians worked on mapping out possible space trajectories the craft could follow to reach its target. A great range of such space highways are calculated with the help of powerful computers to find feasible combinations of launch conditions, spacecraft weight, etc. The best route or routes are not chosen until the time for launch nears.

Electronic engineers designed equipment for the spacecraft to send signals to earth from millions of miles away. They designed equipment for the ground stations to allow engineers on earth to contact and guide the ship in space. Mechanical engineers designed special linkages for moving parts of the system. Some parts, for instance, start out folded in place during launch and are extended only after the spacecraft separates from its booster.

---

* The Cape Canaveral name did not change to Cape Kennedy until after the assassination of President John F. Kennedy, when Congress passed a special bill on November 28, 1963.

Temperature control under the extreme conditions of outer space was a critical consideration. Thermal engineers had to calculate the heat balance of the complete Mariner. They worked out special coatings or cooling devices to make sure the temperature around sensitive parts never became too high or too low or the equipment might stop working. This was a rugged assignment, for there was little or no information then available on how surfaces were affected in outer space. Despite hundreds of hours of testing and computer analysis, the thermal engineers and designers had to base their final decisions partly on educated guesses. These were just a few of the many factors that had to be taken into account in the NASA-JPL development program.

At the same time, a joint NASA-JPL scientific committee discussed possible experiments with leading scientists throughout the country. From the dozens of possible experiments that could be done, a handful had to be selected, since the Mariner A could carry only about fifty to sixty pounds of scientific instruments. As the decisions were made about which tests would be run, the scientists had to brief the Mariner designers in order to integrate the needs of the experiments with the vehicle design. The designer, in turn, might request that the instrument system be modified to prevent its complicating the spacecraft design.

One of the first decisions had to be the choice of booster systems. The thrust available in the launch engines determines how much spacecraft weight can be sent to a planet. The most powerful system in use in 1961 was the combination of the Atlas D booster, made by General Dynamics/Astronautics, and the Agena B upper stage, produced by Lockheed Missiles & Space Company. Looking toward 1962, NASA-JPL designers could see that the Atlas D would still be the most powerful of its type then available. However, on the horizon was a much more powerful upper stage, the Centaur, being developed for NASA by General Dynamics/Astronautics.

Centaur was based on the use of a new fuel, liquid hydrogen, that could provide higher thrust (for the same vehicle weight) over any fuel used before. The most common space booster propellants up to then were either liquid oxygen (LOX) combined with kerosene fuel, or

As Earth and its neighboring planets all pursue their different orbits around the sun, the distance between them changes constantly. These curves show the changes for the 1960–65 period. Because of this, launches from Earth to other planets must be carefully timed to take advantage of the close approach of the target planet. The Table shows the years during the 1960–70 period when positions were favorable for sending spaceships to Venus or Mars.

1960 —		MARS
1961 —	VENUS	
1962 —	VENUS	MARS
1963 —		
1964 —	VENUS	MARS
1965 —	VENUS	
1966 —		MARS
1967 —	VENUS	
1968 —		MARS
1969 —	VENUS	
1970 —	VENUS	

Launch Opportunities for Venus and Mars

unsymmetrical dimethyl hydrazine (UDMH) fuel combined with an oxidizer of inhibited red-fuming nitric acid. The oxidizer is the material that provides oxygen to support combustion. The first pair of propellants is used in the Atlas D and the second pair in the Agena B. Theoretically, the Centaur combination of liquid hydrogen as fuel and liquid oxygen as the oxidizer would permit up to a forty-percent gain in energy potential over either of the more conventional propellant combinations.

Therefore, scientists knew that the use of liquid hydrogen could permit a major breakthrough in the amount of payload that could be sent into space. If a Centaur upper stage could be used, the Mariner vehicle could weigh close to 1,000 pounds. Without the Centaur, only half this weight could be allowed. Centaur, then, represented a key building block to the space program, not just for Mariner but for moon exploration work as well. Actually, the use of liquid-hydrogen fuel is important to the future possibility of military missions as well. The first contract to develop Centaur was given by the military Advanced Research Projects Agency to General Dynamics/Astronautics on November 14, 1958. The program was transferred to NASA in 1959 only when it could be seen that such a vehicle had much more immediate importance in the space effort.

By 1961, Centaur hardware was already reaching the test stage, and NASA and JPL felt the rocket would probably be ready for use by early 1962. It was then decided to design Mariner A with a Centaur upper stage. Throughout most of 1961, JPL designers worked long hours on a sophisticated 990-pound craft, replete with folding booms for special scientific experiments. Even though weight still had to be monitored closely, they were willing to add a pound or two here or there in extra electronic equipment or special sensors to provide the more detailed information the scientists desired.

The pace was rugged but not quite hectic. Both NASA and JPL felt they were doing a superior job in getting such a complicated craft completed in about one year's time. As the summer of 1961 came into view, there were disturbing signs—but not from Mariner A. That was progressing quite satisfactorily. The development of Centaur was in difficulty.

CHAPTER 3

I N MID-1961, the Centaur program was definitely falling behind schedule, but through no fault of its designers. The
Centaur was pioneering a completely new technology. The
liquid-hydrogen fuel it was to use is far trickier to work with than even
liquid oxygen, which must be kept at below —297° F. if it is to remain
a liquid. In order for the hydrogen to be turned into a liquid from its
gaseous state, it must be cooled to the almost unbelievably low temperature of —423° F. If its temperature goes just a degree or two above
this, the hydrogen vaporizes back to a gas. More important is the fact
that hydrogen gas can escape through cracks just millionths of an inch
wide—cracks through which gaseous oxygen would not pass.

Licking these known problems as well as some unexpected ones
was taking more time than the engineers had thought it would. One
such unexpected problem was the brittleness of Centaur tank welds.
Both Atlas and Centaur are made of very thin, welded steel skins. The
type 301 steel used on the Atlas actually became stronger at liquid-

oxygen temperature than it was at room temperature. It was thought that this made it a perfect material for Centaur as well. However, it developed that though type 301 steel did get stronger at temperatures even below that of liquid oxygen, just before reaching —423° F., it suddenly becomes extremely brittle where it has been welded. This problem was eventually solved by spraying nickel into the weld areas so that type 301 steel had the local properties of a more ductile steel. All this took time, however, and by September 1961 it was apparent that Centaur would not be ready when the 1962 launch window arrived. Mariner A had to be cancelled!

Hurried conferences were held in both California and Washington, D.C. The program was reanalyzed and possible alternatives were studied. The JPL Mariner Project Director Jack James asked his staff for estimates of how long it would take to redesign the Mariner for a less powerful launch vehicle. There were now only three to four months in which to accomplish what had previously taken close to a year.

At first, as JPL's chief of Spacecraft Development Section W. J. Schimandle recalls, it was hoped to solve the problem just by stripping down the prototype to meet the weight requirements. However, studies showed this couldn't be done. The next idea was to start with the basic structure of the Ranger III lunar probe and build a Venus vehicle around it. A two-week study showed this approach to be feasible, and it was recommended. NASA then gave the go-ahead for work on two craft, Mariners I and II, each having about half the weight of Mariner A and using an Atlas D-Agena B launch vehicle.

In the end, Schimandle notes, Mariners I and II turned out almost completely different from Mariner A. The latter had nineteen experiments plus articulating booms and complex cabling and electronics. Mariner II carried only six experiments, all in much simpler form. The redesign seemed to be a blessing in disguise, though, for it led to a vehicle probably more reliable than Mariner A would have been yet still carrying most of the essential data-gathering equipment.

The first step was to complete the preliminary design, which usually takes a good many months. The preliminary design is a series of engineers' drawings and specification tables giving the broad outline of the over-all vehicle. The various design teams then figure out in detail the different parts and systems needed to make the completed craft. Mariner A had required three months to set up its preliminary designs. But JPL met the challenge of the new preliminary designs for Mariner I and II in just one week.

The chips were down. The NASA-JPL team had to fight not only the calendar, since the first two Mariners had to be built and ready for testing by mid-January 1962, but the weighing scale also had to be kept in mind. The Atlas D-Agena B system could normally send 400 pounds of payload into space. By pushing its capability to the limit, it might be possible to up the payload to 446 or 447 pounds. And this weight had to include all the structure and systems to take Mariner the 180,-000,000 miles to Venus, meaning very close design was needed if there was to be any room left for the experiments. Without these experiments there obviously was no sense in sending the craft anywhere.

It was no longer a case of letting a pound or two of extra weight remain in a part or a system. No extra weight could be tolerated! The Mariner's designers had to fight not only for every extra pound but for every ounce. The first rough estimate indicated that only twenty-five pounds would be allowed for all the scientific instruments. But the thoroughness with which the vehicle was being developed permitted lightening its structure fifteen more pounds by January to raise the instrument allowance to forty pounds.

To do all this in the time allotted called for every bit of brainpower and energy the scientists and engineers could muster. The forty-hour workweek has not been very common even during the relatively more leisurely Mariner A schedule; for the redesign operation, the idea of a forty-hour week disappeared altogether. Scientists, engineers and laboratory technicians worked sixty, eighty and one hundred hours a week, often coming in during the hours between midnight and dawn, when necessary. In some cases, it was not unusual for key people to stay at the job for days on end, sleeping on makeshift cots whenever a few hours could be sandwiched in.

For instance, system tests might be run on sample parts around the clock to make sure everything worked properly. If a test of a part showed it did not do what it was supposed to do, the design engineers had to spend many more hours over the drawing board to come up with a different, more satisfactory and effective version. Technicians then had to build a new part quickly from the drawings to meet the next round of tests.

Fancy attachments, such as articulating booms, had to be eliminated. Many experiments required the sensitive instruments to operate so that they would not pick up false signals from the vehicle itself. This could be done in different ways. One way was to insulate the instrument from the rest of the structure. Another solution preferred by the scientists was to remove the instrument from the craft body by means of expandable booms. Ways had to be found to manipulate the boom arm either by telescoping it or articulating it. (An articulated boom unfolds like a human arm about one pivot joint or a series of pivot joints.) All of this added weight to Mariner A. In the redesign process, some of the instruments requiring booms were eliminated. In other installations ways were found to isolate the instruments without booms.

One of the boom-mounted instruments was the magnetometer, a device used to measure the magnetic particles in space, particularly to determine whether a planet is surrounded by a magnetic field. However, several of the devices in space vehicles have magnetic fields of their own. In fact, many electronic systems *require* small magnetic fields to work properly. In addition, many structural metals have a certain amount of magnetic force built into their atomic structure. As far as the magnetometer is concerned, the magnetic fields on the vehicle actually are more concentrated and much stronger than the lines of magnetic force in space.

Thus, if the magnetometer is overexposed to the vehicle's magnetic forces, it records them rather than the outside magnetic fields the scientists really wish to measure. The best way to isolate the magnetometer is to put it on the end of a boom, as far away from the structure

24

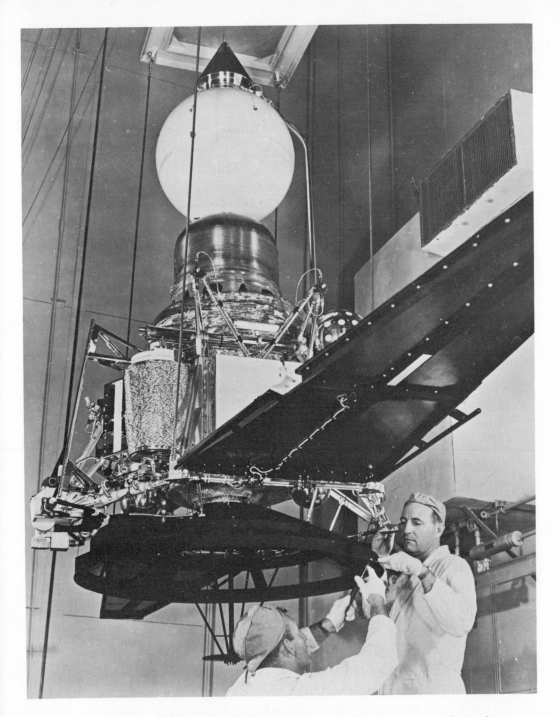

A short cut to arriving at the new Mariner craft was to use the basic design already worked out for the Ranger moon probe program. Here JPL technicians are shown working on the Ranger 3 model, which was used as the basis for the revised Mariner vehicle.

as possible. If this isn't possible, as happened with Mariner I and II, extremely careful study of the instrument's installation is required.

In Mariners I and II, the magnetometer was finally located at the end of a tubular structure extending away from the main part of the vehicle; and nonmetallic materials were used to attach the instrument to the structure. Such materials act as insulation to prevent any magnetic lines of force from passing from the metal body to the instrument, further aiding in keeping all magnetic effects aboard the vehicle to a minimum. In addition, the designers had to work to balance out magnetic fields among the electronic systems so the effects of one would cancel out those of another.

The designers also had to consider the installation problems of the other five experiment instruments chosen to be put on the Mariner besides the magnetometer. These had to be located where they would perform their missions properly without adding to the weight of the craft. A prime need here was an analysis of look angles. This involved drawing a series of charts giving the field of view of the various instruments and control sensors in the different positions of the craft during its voyage. From these charts, engineers could see if the field of view of one instrument or sensor would be blocked by part of the structure or another instrument at any time during flight. When the charts indicated this would happen, either the device was relocated or the structure was redesigned to solve the problem.

As far as the basic structure was concerned, the first step taken was to see if different materials could be used to save weight. The Mariner A structure had been made almost completely of aluminum alloys, since aluminum is one of the lighter metals; but even aluminum was too heavy for the needs of the new vehicle. Therefore, magnesium was substituted for aluminum wherever possible. The same part made of magnesium is only about two-thirds the weight of an aluminum part. This use of magnesium permitted almost a thirty-percent saving in weight. (However, magnesium is limited in the amount of stress it can take without breaking. Thus, where the loads were very high, the aluminum had to be retained.)

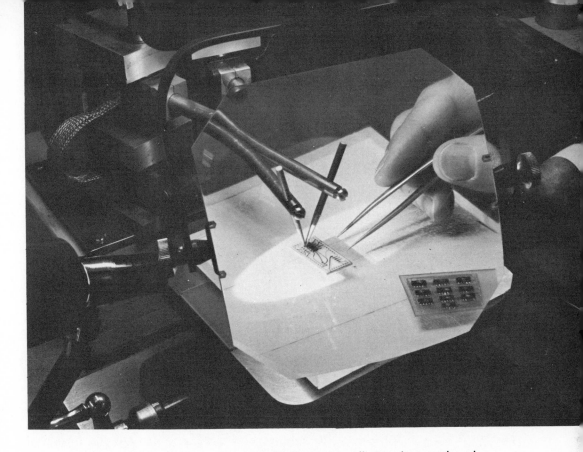

The assembly of a missile or a spacecraft starts small. For the complex electronic equipment, for instance, wires finer than human hair must sometimes be welded to a circuit board under a high-powered magnifying board.

The basic vehicle structure is called the bus. It was hexagonal in shape and made mainly of magnesium plus some aluminum tubing. To the tubing assembly were riveted a series of plates with bolt holes. Six magnesium cases or boxes, containing all the electronic equipment needed both for the scientific experiments and for running the vehicle, were bolted to the plates. The central computer and sequencer (a digital computer) was a key part of this electronic gear.

The computer, an electronic brain, is the heart of the spacecraft's operation in space. Among other things, it times and controls the working of the Mariner propulsion system, turns the experiments on and off, and routes information to a data encoder for relay back to receiving stations on earth. The computer does some of its tasks automatically based on "preprogrammed" information—that is, information put into it by engineers before the launching. Other computer tasks are performed on the receipt of radio commands from earth control stations.

The power to run the craft's many systems comes from the sun. This is achieved by means of thousands of small solar cells installed on two paddles extending out from the central bus. A solar cell is a device that converts energy from sunlight directly into electricity. The electricity then flows through the many tiny electric wires interconnecting the banks of cells to the electric systems of the spacecraft. During launch, though, the paddles are folded and power must come instead from a silver-zinc battery installed in one of the hexagon cases. The thirty-three-pound battery starts out well-charged so that it can provide the needed power from launch time until the paddles are opened and turned toward the sun to energize the solar cells. After Mariner is on its way, the battery serves as an emergency power source.

The solar-panel support structure was made of a series of thin, lightweight, spot-welded aluminum ribs. The panels were attached to the bus so they could each rotate around pivots in two cast-magnesium fittings. During launch, the panels were folded against the tubular structure and held in place at their top edges by small pins. The pins were to be pulled on command from the computer after Mariner separated from its launching craft, thereby allowing the panels to rotate down and latch into the open position.

Above the bus, the designers planned an aluminum tubing superstructure. At its top, the superstructure supported one of the two antennas Mariners I and II would use to beam signals to earth or to receive instructions from the ground stations. The magnetometer sensor was installed at the top of this structure. The tubing also served as the support for the other instruments: the radiometers, the particle-flux detectors (relatives of the geiger counter), and the ion chamber. The role of the radiometers was to measure Venus' surface temperature and get information about its cloud layer; the flux detectors and ion cham-

28

ber were installed to measure charged particles from the sun as they exist in interplanetary space.

Before any of the actual parts for the spacecrafts could be made, many tests and analyses had to be run. Many nonflight models were made to check out the different operational factors involved. For instance, early in the design, small balsa-wood models were made of the tubular structure. By twisting or applying various forces to these models, the engineers could gain a rough idea of the best arrangement of the parts. As time went on, full structural scale models were made to undergo rugged testing in special test chambers. These tests were calculated to subject the models to conditions more rigorous than anything the ship was expected to experience in operation. A wood-and-metal mockup was also made. The engineers made sure that all the parts in this full-scale model would fit properly into the final craft by constructing each part to the dimensions specified in their drawings.

CHAPTER 4

S LOWLY, day after day, more and more pieces of the final
Mariner were okayed for manufacture. As the end of 1961
drew closer, parts returned from the shops for assembly into
the actual Mariner, and the pace picked up. The goal was to have the
first complete Mariner in the main assembly building at JPL by January
15, 1962, with the second one to follow it closely by January 29.
Enough spare parts to make the third back-up vehicle were also due
for delivery by mid-February. The detailed testing could begin only
after these parts arrived. It would take four months of almost around-
the-clock testing to make sure all the complex systems worked together
properly before the first craft could be shipped to the launching pad.

But, as the real Mariners were being assembled, still another full-
scale model was also being made. In many ways, this model was the
most critical of all. Its function was to provide the final checkout of the
temperature control design. In the region of space near Venus, the

Critical part of Mariner pre-flight testing is the thermal control series. Here a full-scale model is shown supported by cables in a special stainless-steel vacuum chamber. The chamber is 47 feet high by 25 feet in diameter and, when its doors revolve into closed position, special pumps take out all the air to leave a vacuum approaching the emptiness of space.

During vacuum chamber thermal control tests, a JPL technician checks Mariner operation under these conditions. He wears a special protective garment.

intensity of solar radiation is almost twice that of the earth. Mariner could not afford the extra weight a cooling system would take up. Protection against the temperature extremes of space had to be provided by a careful arrangement of paint colors, spring-operated louvers* and special metal polishing or insulating material. Since different pieces of equipment in the spacecraft gave off different amounts of heat, careful analysis of the heat balance had to be made.

This balance was achieved by placing models with different thermal coatings into special test chambers that would subject the model to what was thought to be the conditions in space. Tests with a small model were started by November 6, 1961. The goal for beginning the full-scale-model testing was the end of February 1962. Thermal control engineers made hundreds of runs. The procedure was to find the heat given off by each electronic or mechanical part and then figure out what coatings could be applied to various areas in order to balance this heat against the sun's radiation. Each time the model was coated with a different combination of colors and placed in the cold-wall vacuum chamber. The test chamber simulated the cold emptiness of outer space, and duplicated what the surfaces of the craft would "see" when pointed away from the sun.

On the other hand, the surface facing the sun had to be able to withstand the heat of solar radiation. To simulate this, special heating units were attached to these surfaces. After each test run, thermal engineers examined the results to discover which spacecraft areas had the wrong heating values (the surfaces might be too hot or too cold) and adjusted the coating pattern to conform to this data. Run after run had to be made, since changing one or two parts of the system also changed the heat values in other parts of the craft. Besides, as the weeks went by design changes kept occurring in some of the equipment, causing still more changes in the temperature patterns.

Even though full-scale-model tests were being held by early 1962, the engineers were still faced with too many unknowns for comfort.

* Louvers are a series of slats set in a frame, and are sometimes movable. They resemble venetian blinds or old-fashioned window shutters.

The Agena upper stage, developed by Lockheed Missiles and Space Co. for the U. S. Air Force, provides the "push" to place Mariner in orbit, then launch it toward Venus. Here an Agena is being hoisted into position for mating with an Atlas during an Air Force missile launch.

Such things as finding the correct thermal pattern were perplexing. The simulators used were ingenious, but they just could not reproduce the exact conditions of interplanetary space. Paint coatings, for instance, are affected in various ways by radiation, and this radiation could cause unexpected changes in the thermal properties of the coating. The coating might radiate more, or possibly less, heat than is allowed for, if its chemical composition were to change in space operation. In the end, the Mariner designers knew that the answers could come only from flight experience. In this sense, the entire Mariner voyage was going to be a major experiment.

Finally, the flight thermal-control pattern was agreed on. It included black paint on the back of the solar panels, gold coatings on the magnesium parts, white stripes on the fiber glass omnidirectional antenna (at the top of the superstructure) and special white paint (made of zinc sulphate) on other parts of the apparatus. Most of the aluminum surfaces did not need coatings; instead, they were polished brightly to reflect as much heat as possible. In addition, a special heat shield of Mylar plastic was sewn across the top surface of the hexagonal bus to provide a sunshade for the electronic equipment.

As Mariner Spacecraft Systems Manager Dan Schneiderman put it, "We at JPL never really got enough flights to assure a perfect Mariner probe. To test an instrument of Mariner's importance and cost properly, we should have had at least a dozen preliminary shots. Of course, we milked all the knowledge we could from previous space launches. We looked at Explorer, Pioneer and Vanguard results in preparing for Mariner. All technology from past shots was sifted and examined. But that wasn't enough—because no past space probes by the United States had attempted what we were now trying to do with the Mariner."

As the temperature tests continued and the Mariner vehicle neared its final assembly, scientists in other sections of JPL and NASA were also summing up what had been found out about Venus by tests run from the earth. Earlier in the year, from March to May of 1961, a radar bounce program had been carried out in preparation for Mariner. This program consisted of bouncing radar signals off Venus and carefully timing how long it took for the echoes to return to earth. The scientists could figure this out from the distance between earth and Venus, since they knew how fast the radar wave was traveling. Their main goal, however, was to refine the main scientific yardstick of the universe, the astronomical unit. This is the mean distance from the earth to the sun and is the basis on which all planetary relationships are calculated. Up to 1961, the astronomical unit (or AU) was known only to within an error of approximately 60,000 miles. A much more accurate value was now needed to make the precise calculations for the Mariner trajectory. The 1961 radar tests narrowed this error to only about plus-or-minus 300 miles—a more acceptable figure.

The series of radar bounces also gave them a better idea as to Venus' precise orbit, another important factor in plotting the Mariner course. Since Mariner was aimed from earth to reach Venus some three to four months after launch, it was important to know approximately where Venus would be at that time. The new data indicated that the planet rotated at a very slow rate, perhaps once every 225 days (which is also the length of the Venusian year). This showed that Venus always keeps the same surface toward the sun, in much the same way that our moon has only one side always facing the earth.

Radar tests, coupled with data gathered by astronomers from Venus photographs and from analysis of the energy spectrum given off by the planet, provided all the available information about Venus up to the time of the Mariner launch. Naturally, some of the information was sketchy and open to argument. For instance, several scientists said the energy spectrum showed Venus had a surface temperature of 615° F. But other scientists felt this calculation was incorrectly based on reflections from dense clouds of charged particles in Venus' atmosphere. If the second theory were true, the planet's surface temperature was, by earth standards, close to a livable climate. One thing was clear: Venus was covered with thick clouds. Spectrographic studies of Venus indicated the clouds probably were composed primarily of carbon dioxide. Changes in shadings seen through powerful telescopes—strange dark and light markings appearing on the top cloud layer—indicated there might be breaks in the clouds. But no one could be too sure of this. The major purpose of Mariner's Venus experiments was to help settle such questions.

It was natural, then, that excitement in the scientific communities mounted as the launch date for Mariner I came closer and closer. But everyone knew how many hurdles had to be passed over and how tremendous the odds were that all of the thousands of factors involved would mesh perfectly. A failure in one tiny transistor, a few dabs of thermal control paint in the wrong spot, even a slip of a decimal point in a mathematical calculation could cause the entire multimillion-dollar mission to go up in smoke.

By February 26, 1962, the full-scale thermal model was undergoing vacuum-chamber tests at JPL. The complete flight models were being run through system test after system test. Banks of computers fed hypothetical mission data into the hexagon boxes on the Mariner bus. Engineers watched to see if the Mariner computer opened the control valves at the right time and that the control sensors rolled the vehicle as they were supposed to do.

Runs were made using the mid-course correction engine system. The mid-course correction was perhaps the most crucial point of the trajectory. It was highly unlikely that when the Mariner was shot out of the parking orbit by the Agena B rocket that its course would be accurately aligned for a close pass-by of the planet. There were too many variables; too much brute force was involved at the moment of launch to calculate more than a rough path toward Venus. Therefore, provision had been made in the craft for making one major course correction a few days after it was on its way to Venus, and a special rocket engine was installed for this purpose. Using an anhydrous hydrazine liquid propellant, the thirty-seven-pound engine was located in the center of the hexagonal bus. The doorknob-shaped fuel tank used a nitrogen pressure system to force fuel into the thrust chamber. In operation, the central computer opened the valve from a small gaseous-nitrogen tank to let nitrogen flow into the top of the tank.

There the gas pushed against a rubber bladder which separated the nitrogen from the fuel. This would make the bladder expand and force the fuel into the engine. The engine would then develop fifty pounds of thrust for a maximum time of fifty-seven seconds. There was just enough fuel for this one maneuver. Thus, many simulated tests of this maneuver were done on the ground to weed out any flaws in the design.

By the middle of May, all the major shakedown tests, including a rugged vibration test of the entire vehicle, were nearly completed. This work not only helped engineers and scientists find errors and correct them, but it also provided invaluable training for the people who would man the control stations of the Deep Space Instrumentation Facility (DSIF). The five DSIF stations would monitor the information from Mariner once it was space-borne and relay commands to it from the earth.

The first phase of the momentous undertaking was over. By the beginning of June, Mariner I and II and the backup craft were on their way to Cape Canaveral. Their destination was Launch Complex 12. Special truck trailers and planes brought the other parts of the system to the complex, including the mightly Atlas D booster and the Agena B second stage. Now came more weeks of testing on every part of the system until the entire vehicle, with the Mariner I on top, inside its protective shroud, finally stood assembled and ready on the launch pad.

CHAPTER 5

B Y JULY 19, 1962, all seemed in order for this country's first Venus space probe. At Cape Canaveral and throughout the worldwide tracking network of the DSIF, NASA engineers, scientists and technicians prepared for the hectic hours of the final countdown. Though monitoring of the Venus flight would be handled by the NASA-JPL-DSIF team, the launch itself was supervised by the U.S. Air Force Space Systems Division.

In anticipation of a successful shot, the public relations staff of JPL and NASA sent to the press "Hold for Release" stories of the launch operation. The next evening, the countdown began at 11:33 P.M. Eastern Standard Time at a value of T minus 176 minutes. This meant it would take a total of 176 minutes to go over all the parts of the system before the engines could be lighted for lift-off.

Soundlessly, electronic checkout equipment sent streams of electric current through different parts of the system to see if all were working

41

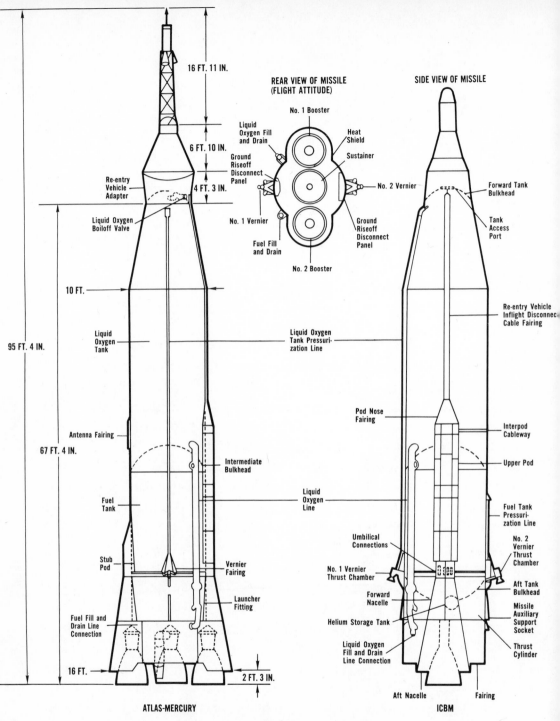

Three-View of the Atlas Series D Missile

Main features of the Atlas booster are shown in these drawings of the D series used to launch the manned Mercury capsule. A similar Atlas was chosen for Mariner II.

properly. The radio circuits in the Mariner, the guidance system in the Atlas, the restart engine system in Agena, and dozens of other sections of the vehicle were checked in turn. As each part responded correctly, a green light lit up on the consoles in the launch-control center. At the same time the vehicle was being checked out, similar checks were being run throughout the launch-operation facilities, from the range-safety equipment to the DSIF's.

Inevitably, somewhere in the series of green lights, a red light glowed. Something had been found that was out of order. The hold signal went out and the countdown stopped until the flaw was found and repaired.

The first such hold cropped up at T minus 165 minutes and counting was stopped until past midnight. At 12:37 A.M. it started again and proceeded steadily to T minus 79 minutes. Then, another in the frustrating delays that launch control crews must become used to occurred. A fuse had blown in the range safety circuits. This time, the countdown had to be abandoned altogether and launching was rescheduled for the following evening. At 11:08 P.M. on July 21, the entire procedure began again. This time, some extra checks had been added, upping the countdown starting time to T minus 200 minutes.

Once more holds appeared. At T minus 130 (12:17 A.M., July 22) a component in the ground-tracking system had to be replaced. After 41 minutes, counting was resumed. Several other holds cropped up in the hours that followed, but none posed enough problems to wash out the launch.

Finally, at 4:21 A.M. EST, the final second arrived. The controller pushed the fire button and jets of flame shot from the three nozzles of the Atlas engine. The Mariner vehicle rose effortlessly into the air and the hundreds of people in the control center heaved one vast sigh of relief.

But five minutes later their faces mirrored deep apprehension. The booster was not following the right path. It was veering to the northeast, a dangerous move that could cause the booster to drop off outside its range area, possibly in inhabited territory. Apparently there

Looking aft from the cargo plane, the nose end of the Atlas is seen being moved toward the cabin. Soon the plane will be winging its way toward Cape Kennedy, Florida.

had been an error in the guidance equations (the mathematical orders given the computer to tell it where to direct the missile). Only six seconds were needed to separate the Agena and Mariner and send Mariner heavenward—but the launch officer couldn't take a chance. He pressed the *destruct* button and explosive charges in the Atlas shattered the craft into thousands of glowing fragments.

Even though everyone knew how many obstacles there always were to the success of such a complicated mission, the letdown was tremendous. The hours of painstaking work, the often tedious and frustrating job of perfecting each minute part of the system—all had gone for naught. But the failure had not been a total loss. From each setback, engineers gain more experience about what has to be done to make future launches more likely to succeed. After the first few days, feelings of despair faded away. Everyone settled down to prepare for the Mariner II try.

More weeks of testing followed. The information from the first shot, recorded on electronic tape from the Atlas, Agena and Mariner radio signals, was carefully examined to see what had to be changed. The new target date was late August or early September.

Meanwhile, across the world, Russian technicians quietly readied their own challenge. They had the advantage of much more powerful boosters; boosters that could hurl a larger spacecraft into space. This time, they erected a four-stage launch vehicle on top of which they were going to place a Venus probe twice Mariner's weight. Theoretically, the extra-weight capability gave them more of a margin for error. But they also had leeway to put in extra equipment so that if one system failed another could take over. Their target date, too (a well-kept secret), was late August.

At Cape Canaveral, the scenes of the previous June were being repeated. In hangar AE, a "safe" area in a rugged concrete bunker, the mid-course-maneuver engine was installed in Mariner II and the long series of tests and examinations had begun. The new Atlas-Agena booster system also moved toward the launch pad. As the days went by and the last week of August came into view, a protective shroud was placed around Mariner and it was moved out to the gantry of Complex 12.

A huge crane picked up Mariner and carried it up past the waiting booster. Mariner was carefully placed on top of Agena, then lowered into place and bolted down. Complete systems tests were run and once more all was *go* for the second U.S. Venus launch. On August 25, at 6:43 P.M. EST, the countdown began. This time the checkout was over 200 minutes. When it reached T minus 205, though, a defect had been found in the battery in the Agena. After strenuous efforts to correct the trouble, the launch was cancelled till the next day.

Meanwhile, in the Soviet Union, all was *go* for their probe and the Russian craft shot up through the skies into a parking orbit. If the

45

space ship could now be launched into a Venus trajectory, it would beat Mariner there by nearly a week. But once more fate intervened. The Russian probe could not be separated from its upper stage. Their attempt had failed.

On August 26, at 6:37 P.M., the countdown was started for Mariner II. At T minus 100, the Atlas main battery showed a flaw; close to an hour was required to change it. This time, however, the countdown could continue. As minute after minute passed by and the clock hands moved toward midnight, the hopes of the launch crew rose higher and higher. Green light after green light flashed. Routine holds were inserted to double check such things as the Atlas battery, but no major malfunctions appeared. Midnight came and went—soon it was only five minutes to launch. Then came a hold for trouble in the radio-guidance system. As soon as it was fixed, the count resumed, only to be stopped as the guidance system acted up again.

Finally, all was ready. It was 1:15 A.M., then 1:30. The men at the launch consoles perspired freely. At 1:43 the last second arrived and the fire button was depressed. All 360,000 pounds of the Atlas' thrust labored to push its precious package skyward. This time the missile was on course—the trajectory equations were on the button. For an agonizing moment, the ground instruments indicated that the vehicle was starting to roll ominously. If the roll continued, Mariner II might share the fate of its twin.

But the craft righted itself and the Agena soon separated from the burned-out Atlas. Separation was accomplished by means of small explosive charges. Agena's engine was not scheduled to start firing until the upper stage had coasted a bit on the momentum given it by the booster. Just before separation, the protective shroud to prevent friction-heat was jettisoned by eight spring-loaded bolts.

At 1:58.53 A.M. the Agena engine cut in to carry itself and Mariner to an orbiting speed of 18,000 miles per hour. This task was accomplished, by 2:01.12 A.M. With the combined craft swinging around the earth in a parking orbit some 116.19 miles above the surface, Agena's engine cut off. This left the fuel tanks with enough propellant for the engine to restart in orbit when the central computer on board gave the signal.

By now, tracking stations on earth were following the progress of the craft. However, all the actions up to the point of injection of the ship into its path toward Venus were initiated by plans stored in the computer on board. The DSIF stations would not take over until Mariner was on its way.

At 26 minutes 3.08 seconds after lift-off, the Agena started again, propelling itself and Mariner into a course toward Venus. At this time, Agena-Mariner was at a point over the South Atlantic, roughly midway between the coasts of Brazil and Africa. Two minutes later, with the two vehicles traveling at about 25,420 miles per hour, Agena stopped firing and spring-loaded bolts separated the two.

CHAPTER 6

A
T LAST, Mariner was free to start its historic journey. Now the work of the DSIF tracking network began. For a time, the craft would continue to be controlled automatically by its own computer. However, the system permitted DSIF controllers to send an override signal to the vehicle if the Mariner didn't seem to be progressing as desired. Now DSIF also had to keep a close watch on the spacecraft in preparation for the critical mid-course maneuver. If the maneuver was not performed perfectly, Mariner would miss Venus by several hundred thousand miles instead of the desired 10,000 or 20,000 miles.

Riding herd on the five DSIF stations was JPL's Spacecraft Flight Operations Director Tom Bilbo. From his headquarters at JPL's Space Flight Operations Center (SFOC) in Pasadena, California, he was in constant contact with the five DSIF stations. DSIF number one was a mobile van-type tracker located near Johannesburg, South Africa. Its role was mainly to be in a position to track the craft during low-altitude flight. The other four stations included the Pioneer site at Goldstone, California; Echo site (also at Goldstone); Woomera, Australia; and Johannesburg, South Africa. Data sent to the stations from Mariner was immediately relayed to Pasadena for processing in the JPL large-capacity 7090 computer.

Besides these contacts, Tom Bilbo could also get in touch quickly with all the key engineering groups at JPL by closed-circuit TV. These groups included a scientific-data group, a spacecraft-data analysis team, a tracking-data analysis group, an orbit-determination group and a mid-course-command group. These groups could also make contact with Bilbo on their own if they had something important to discuss.

As the clocks at the control centers showed 44 minutes had elapsed from launch time, the Mariner computer signaled its having made the first major step in the Venus journey. It caused explosives to fire and pull the pins holding the solar panels against the superstructure. The spring-actuated panels moved down into place, their almost 10,-000 cells now ready to collect vital energy from the sun. The same operation freed the radiometer that would scan Venus' cloud cover three and a half months later.

The next critical maneuver was to align the Mariner so that its flight axis would be pointed in the right direction—always keeping the solar panels turned toward the sun and the radiometers in a position to scan Venus. To do this, small earth and sun sensors were used to send signals to actuate a series of ten small gas jets. These small jets used nitrogen-gas propulsion to turn the craft in one direction or another.

At 60 minutes after launch, the computer turned on the sensor system and the sun sensors began turning the gas jets on and off. The craft jockeyed until its long axis was pointed toward the sun. With its solar panels now working, the Mariner electric system had the extra energy it needed to run the scientific and other electronic systems. The next alignment of the probe vehicle had to wait a few days. This was to be the critical reception of earth transmissions by the four-foot-diameter high-gain antenna located under the spacecraft hexagonal bus.

The several days of delay were due to the fact that the earth sensor—a three-section, optical photomultiplier tube that sought out earth and aligned the antenna—was too sensitive to be used earlier.

During these early maneuvers, NASA-JPL scientists got the first inkling that the flight would be a struggle all the way. As Operations Director Bilbo relates it, "The science experiments turn-on was the first cliff-hanger. The turn-on was scheduled for when Mariner II was almost over Johannesburg. The moment came for this to happen, but the data return did not come through to the earth. It's balance was probably off. In order for Mariner to operate correctly, it had to be in perfect balance between pitch and roll. You might compare this operation to regulating the hot and cold water in a shower bath to just the right temperature while at the same time cutting the flow of water to the desired amount.

"Due to the roll of the craft while sending information back to earth, the signal strength dropped and we couldn't pick it up. Things were happening on Mariner all the time; but because the signal strength from the radio equipment dropped, we didn't know if things were happening properly. Then, suddenly, everything locked perfectly and strong signals came in. For a moment, everyone stopped biting his fingernails."

This was the first indication that the earth sensor was not working as planned. Flight controllers held their breath as Mariner, 167 hours after launch, went through the earth-acquisition step. The earthside computer turned off the scientific instruments for awhile and activated a series of gyroscopes in the attitude-control system. It also ordered the earth sensor to roll the spacecraft about its long axis (held steady with the ship's nose pointed toward the sun) until the high-gain antenna was properly aligned. But instead of actuating the gas jets the sensor switched right over to the antenna.

When relayed to the ground, this information was extremely confusing. The brightness value the sensor indicated showed that it was seeing the moon rather than the earth!

Originally, it had been intended to start the mid-course maneuver shortly after this point. But now the engineers had to delay another day to try to make sure they knew the ship's position. Programs were fed into the computer to see how much it mattered whether the craft antenna pointed to the moon or the earth. The answer was that the earth and moon were almost in a single line of sight from Mariner II and it would have made only 1,200 to 1,500 miles difference. This was considered a minute error since the over-all mileage was being computed in the hundreds of millions.

While all this was going on, tension at the control centers was so high it could almost be cut with a knife. Then, Bilbo's group suddenly found itself cut off from the key DSIF station. "A truck near the Goldstone DSIF ran off the road, hit a telephone pole, and knocked it down," Tom Bilbo remembers. "This would not ordinarily have been very newsworthy out there in the desert—but this pole carried the wires from Goldstone. When it fell it knocked out direct communication. And the connection stayed out for forty-five minutes. During this time, which was right in the middle of transmission, no one at control center knew what was happening on the Mariner." The forty-five minutes seemed like so many years; but when the wires to Goldstone were fixed, it turned out that Mariner was locked properly.

Scientists now fed information to the JPL computer on Mariner's present course and the desired future position after the mid-course maneuver. They checked and rechecked their figures; the commands they sent to reorient the spacecraft had to be right the first time. Once the mid-course engine fired, it could not be used again. Whatever trajectory resulted was the one Mariner would follow all the way to Venus.

There was a certain amount of leeway for the scientists, however. For the instruments to get the proper look at Venus, they had to be somewhere between 8,000 and 40,000 miles above the planet. It was decided to try for a 9,000 to 10,000 miles fly-by. Based on their analyses of information received about Mariner's present course, if about forty-five miles per hour was added to the ship's speed, Mariner II would turn into the correct trajectory. On September 4, the maneuver commands were flashed to Mariner from Goldstone.

Down below, Earth moves farther and farther away. The stages burn out and Agena starts to move Mariner II into a parking orbit.

The first command gave the direction and amount of roll needed, the second the direction and amount of pitch, and the third the increment of speed required. The Mariner transmitter was also ordered to switch from the directional antenna at the craft's base to the omni-directional antenna at its top. This was done because the directional antenna, was positioned under the motor-exhaust nozzle. For the maneuver, the dish-shaped antenna was rotated out of the way to permit the engine to fire. The attitude-control gas jet then fired to move Mariner in roll and pitch as ordered. Next, the mid-course motor ignited—its sudden roar unheard by anyone out in the vast emptiness of space.

The whole maneuver took slightly more than half an hour—about twelve minutes to roll, twenty-two minutes to pitch and less than a minute for engine firing. The controllers on the ground anxiously awaited the results of the maneuver. Was the craft doing as it was told? Had the engine fired properly? Could the shock of firing damage any of the delicate devices on board? During the operation, the earth and sun sensors were unlocked from their targets. Would they resume their positions after the action was completed?

At the proper time, the ground stations waited for the answers to come from the craft's scientific instruments. But just as before, the signal failed to come through. The engineers turned their dials, checked their equipment again and tried once more to make contact. Seconds, then minutes ticked by as the dread thought arose that, perhaps, just as in the Russian Venus probe vehicle, the Mariner transmitter had died. Then, suddenly, the signal came through, loud and clear.

But there were still doubts. With the lapse, NASA and JPL researchers were afraid the signal might be in error. Checks were made and all seemed in order. Rough calculations indicated the maneuver had been perfect and Mariner was on the right course for a 9,000-10,000 mile approach to that distant planet.

The trajectory was taking the spaceship slightly out of the plane of the ecliptic (the ecliptic is the horizontal plane of a planet's orbit in relation to the sun). Mariner had been launched initially in the other

Near Johannesburg, South Africa, the webbed dish of a DSIF antenna faces heavenward.

direction from earth. At the time, Venus had been behind the earth but traveling faster. As Mariner moved in this direction, its speed fell and it was unable to maintain a circular orbit against the sun's gravity. Then the sun slowly "captured" the ship and pulled it inward in a curving path that caused Mariner to pass by earth and eventually catch up with the rapidly moving Venus. As the spaceship moved sunward, Venus caught up with earth and passed it. The trajectory was designed so that Mariner would pass by Venus' dark side at a speed of 83,000 miles per hour.

CHAPTER 7

WITH THE ship inexorably on a path to a final permanent orbit around the sun, it had become apparent to JPL Spacecraft Flight Operations Director Bilbo's group that they would be called on for far more work than they had expected. "We knew definitely now," he notes, "that the spacecraft's performance was abnormal. We were not exactly sure the information we were getting was what it was supposed to be. We had thought that after a reasonable time from launch had elapsed, we could cut our twenty-four-hour-a-day monitoring to ten hours. The data we were getting blew this plan full of holes. We had to go on, around the clock, day after day after day and we were not prepared for it. There just weren't enough qualified people in existence. The human body can take only so much and we were forced to press everyone we could get into the operation.

"It finally boiled down to about eighteen hours a day of work for each qualified engineer and scientist. They were backed up by junior engineers, who, however, had had no previous experience of this sort. The juniors thus received unexpected, accelerated, on-the-job training. It was a gamble—for if a crisis arose, a small error in judgment by an inexperienced hand could have washed out the program. It was a gamble we had to take. But despite the pressure, all neophytes came through in fine style."

After the pulse-quickening events of the mid-course maneuver, for a time Mariner settled on its course without major incident. Well—almost. About ten days after the shift-of-direction maneuver, the scientific instruments on board suddenly stopped transmitting for some unexplained reason. Then, after a lapse, the signals mysteriously started flowing again. "It seemed," said Bilbo, "almost as if Mariner had a mind of its own."

As the miles ticked off—mounting to distances that the human mind finds hard to comprehend—the craft sent back vast amounts of information on the composition of interplanetary space. All four scientific data-gathering instruments aboard Mariner were working normally. The ion chamber-particle flux detector measured the intensity and distribution of the particles in space as they were meant to. The solar-plasma detector recorded the intensity of other low-energy bits of matter, called protons, which flow into space from the sun. The cosmic-dust detector measured the amount of dust present which comes from somewhere outside the solar system. And, finally, the magnetometer checked the structure and changes in magnetic field in deep space.

Every day this steady stream of information was helping the scientists to gain a better idea of the makeup of the universe. It confirmed the existence of such things as a "solar wind" of charged particles flowing regularly through space from the sun.* It showed that radiation levels in the earth-Venus part of space, when solar flares are not present, are well below the danger point for an astronaut.

By September 17, Mariner was over three and a half million miles from earth. By mid-October, the distance was between seven and eight million. As the end of the month came into view, all seemed to be going

---

* See Chapter 8 for further discussion of the composition of the solar wind and plasma.

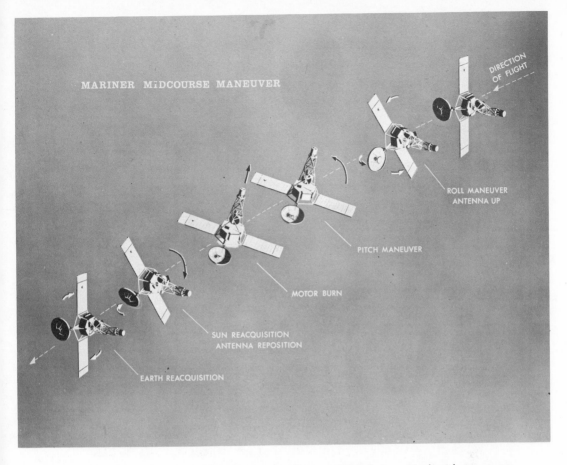

MARINER MIDCOURSE MANEUVER

DIRECTION OF FLIGHT

ROLL MANEUVER
ANTENNA UP

PITCH MANEUVER

MOTOR BURN

SUN REACQUISITION
ANTENNA REPOSITION

EARTH REACQUISITION

Eight days out from Earth, Mariner II goes through its critical mid-course maneuver to correct its path from one which misses Venus by 250,000 miles to one which goes only 21,000 miles from the planet's surface.

well and the control teams began to relax a bit. They had, in the meantime, met with one slight disappointment. Analysis of the tracking data showed Mariner was slightly off the desired trajectory. The speed increase given during the mid-course maneuver had been forty-seven miles per hour instead of forty-five. This changed the path so that Mariner would pass within 21,000 miles of Venus instead of 9,000. However, 21,000 was still well within the working envelope for the Venus instruments.

On October 31, with Mariner 12,000,000 miles away, there appeared to be something wrong with the system supplying power to the instruments. The stored-power level of the solar panels had dropped alarmingly low. Of course, the battery could be used to provide extra power for such an emergency. However, with one whole solar panel apparently not working properly, the load was too much for the battery. The battery charge was falling dangerously low and it was not re-charging. To conserve precious battery life, it was decided to turn off the instruments for several days and see if the battery could recharge itself to the proper level.

On November 8, with Mariner II six weeks away from its objective and 15,000,000 miles away from earth, the order went out from Gold-stone to turn the instruments back on. As the minutes went by, everyone waited with fingers crossed for the power values to register. The reply came from Mariner, and Bilbo's group soon had the word—the system had corrected itself once more and all was working properly. In fact, the data showed the solar panels were both working again.

While Mariner continued with its tightrope performance toward Venus, word came of another major space venture by Russia. On November 1, the Soviets placed a new probe in an earth-parking orbit. The launch command was given, and this time the spacecraft reacted properly. It moved out toward its goal: the planet Mars.

With all of its efforts concentrated on Mariner, JPL had decided not to try for Mars until the next opportunity in late 1964. (Though never officially confirmed, there were persistent reports that two previ-ous Russian Mars probes, launched on October 10 and October 14, 1960, had failed to reach parking orbits.) On November 8, the Soviet news agency Tass reported their Mars I probe was 1.6 million miles from earth and functioning normally. The agency stated that without a premid-course-correction maneuver, the probe would come within 156,-000 miles of the red planet. With the correction, it was expected the ship would come within 620 miles of Mars' surface.

The over-all weight of the Russian probe vehicle gave U.S. en-gineers pause. It grossed 1,965 pounds—over four times the weight of Mariner II—and was almost twice as large as the payload the still-unavailable upper-stage Centaur rocket would be able to put aloft.

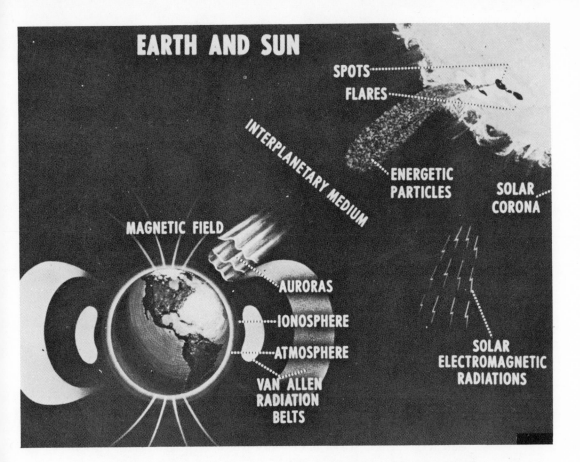

EARTH AND SUN

SPOTS
FLARES
INTERPLANETARY MEDIUM
ENERGETIC PARTICLES
SOLAR CORONA
MAGNETIC FIELD
AURORAS
IONOSPHERE
ATMOSPHERE
VAN ALLEN RADIATION BELTS
SOLAR ELECTROMAGNETIC RADIATIONS

The many amazing effects taking place between the thin orange peel of earth's atmosphere and the sun are shown in this NASA sketch. Such projects as Mariner are helping scientists gain more understanding of these phenomena.

As Mariner moved closer and closer to its objective, a new danger cropped up. The temperature readings from major parts of the equipment began to move dangerously upward. The unknown factors in the thermal-control design had come back to haunt the mission. The paint patterns and the special louvers were not keeping the spacecraft as cool as had been expected. In the meantime, the faulty solar panel had shorted out again and the emergency battery was switched back into the circuit. As the end of November approached, Mariner was still sending information; but the battery had been designed to keep operating at temperatures as high as 125° F., and it had now climbed to

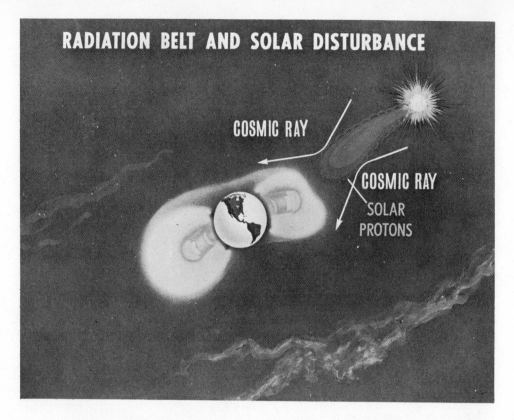

RADIATION BELT AND SOLAR DISTURBANCE

COSMIC RAY

COSMIC RAY

SOLAR PROTONS

Effects of a solar flare are shown in these NASA diagrams by Dr. H. J. Goett, head of Goddard Space Flight Center. A sudden eruption on the sun sends out a huge tongue of magnetic force (*left*). This rapidly expands to speed up cosmic particles (*right*) and compress Earth's magnetic field.

an operating temperature of 113° F. Bilbo's group ran calculations on its probable temperature at Venus arrival and came up with an estimate of 129° F. Still, there usually is some extra allowance in a good design and there was hope the battery would manage to last until after the critical date of December 14.

Troubles, though, come in bunches. Other temperatures were rising sharply, too, and if there was a chance that the battery could resist the heat, something else might short out and put the system out of operation. By late November, the solar panels, for example, were sending signals indicating temperatures of 220° F. against the maximum design limit of 350° F.

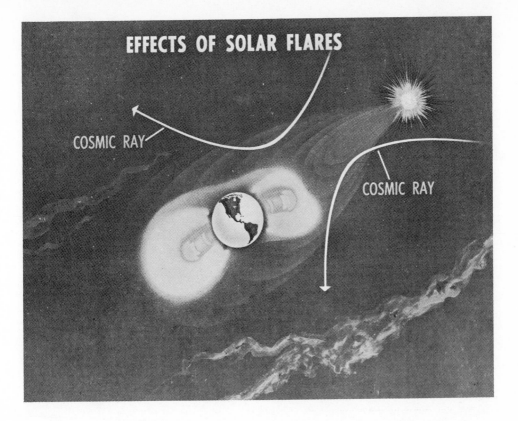

While JPL engineers helplessly watched the changes in Mariner, another report from Russia told of Mars I's progress. On November 28, their probe was 5,632,700 miles from earth and its temperatures were in the range of 75°-80° F.

November gave way to December and Mariner II kept relaying thousands of radio signals to DSIF. The temperatures on board rose degree by degree with each passing day. The battery, solar panels and instruments were all getting hotter and hotter. On December 4, a signal from Mariner showed the earth sensor was at 143° F. This was eighteen degrees above the maximum operating temperature for which it had been designed. Despite this, the sensor still held its focus locked

63

on distant earth. Its parts, though, were losing their sensitivity and might lose sight of earth at any moment, perhaps letting the spacecraft move out of its carefully calculated position, thereby canceling the Venus experiment.

Once again JPL engineers made hurried recalculations. They compared the decline in sensitivity of the sensor with its ability to keep its sights locked on earth. They found that the sensor would remain operating effectively until Mariner was past its Venus encounter.

All the DSIF stations began preparing for the critical Venus approach. If the equipment on Mariner kept working, it would be only a few days before the signal could be sent to activate the planet-scanning radiometers. As December 12 arrived, two days prior to encounter, the temperatures on Mariner had risen so high that six of the temperature sensors had reached their upper limits. The searing heat was more than the sensors could bear and no more information on equipment temperature was sent to earth. The engineers and scientists grimly considered the irony of the Mariner equipment failing now—after almost 180,000,000 miles of flight—just a day or two before the high point of the mission.

But the signals kept on coming as the seconds, minutes and hours passed. December 13 came and went. And as the clock passed the hours of midnight on the Pacific Coast, DSIF prepared to send the order for the craft to take the first close look man had ever taken at a neighboring planet.

It was still touch and go. Twelve hours before the ultimate goal was reached, the Mariner central computer was scheduled to start the Venus-encounter sequence. The earth controllers waited for the spacecraft to show this had been done, but nothing happened. The morning hours of December 14 passed slowly—1 A.M.—2 A.M.—3 A.M.—4 A.M.—still nothing had taken place. Finally, at 5:35 A.M. an emergency signal was sent to Mariner from Goldstone. According to all information available, Mariner would be in position to begin scanning Venus in just six and one-half hours. Thirty-six million miles away, Mariner II received the weak emergency pulse from earth—and responded.

CHAPTER 8

ABOUT 11:15 A.M. on December 14, 1962, the instruments on Mariner picked up the Venus disk and the data started to flow back to the waiting recording equipment on earth. At 11:59.28 A.M., a split second before noon, Mariner reached its closest approach to Venus. It was 21,648 miles above the planet's surface and its signals had to travel 36,000,000 miles to earth.* For close to forty-two minutes, oscillographs, magnetic-tape devices and other sensitive meters took down thousands of signals that scientists would work months and years to decipher and interpret.

Tired, but elated, the JPL team gave Tom Bilbo a World War I

---

* This figure is the actual earth-Venus distance at encounter. However, since the planets and Mariner were all moving during the voyage and Mariner had to catch up with Venus, by the time it arrived at the planet it had traveled a distance of 182,000,000 miles in the 109 days after its launch on August 27.

aviator's helmet and nicknamed him the "ground-based space pilot." A group of JPL people gathered to go to a local restaurant and have a small celebration. But Bilbo never made it. He was too exhausted. He just sank deeper into his console chair and didn't move until, some time later, he struggled to his feet, walked to his car, and drove home. For the first time in months, he and other key project people had a full night of uninterrupted sleep. Many of them, like Bilbo, then headed away from Pasadena for a rest. Says Bilbo, "I departed for the High Sierras where there wasn't any tension and I could do a little hunting and fishing and a lot of just looking up at sky and clouds."

The Mariner kept on sending signals back, monitored by re-placement crews, for about twenty days after its fly-by was over. Then it finally succumbed to the relentless attack of the sun's radiation and fell silent. As the days passed, it moved into a wide orbit around the sun, moving just as do the natural planets in their revolutions around the heart of the solar system.

Now it was the scientists' turn to work overtime. As some eagerly started examining the curves, numbers and other data received from Mariner, others were compiling information from another radar-bounce series that had been started in October to coincide with the Mariner fly-by. The radar information could be combined with some of the Mariner information to give a double-barreled look at such things as Venus' rate of rotation.

Though there wasn't the pressure or urgency that had faced the Mariner flight controllers, it still was a long, often tedious, job to break down the information. Complicated formulas had to be used, most of them requiring the use of computers to achieve solution. Even then, the answers had to be analyzed carefully to make sure the correct meaning was assigned to them. A decimal point in the wrong place or the assumption that the information was from one part of the cloud layer and not another could lead to completely wrong conclusions.

Some of the answers about the nature of Venus could be given almost at once. Thus, on December 28, scientists F. J. Coleman of the University of California at Los Angeles, Prof. Leverett Davis, Jr., of the California Institute of Technology, Dr. E. J. Smith of JPL and Dr. C. P. Sonett of NASA Ames Laboratory reported that the magnetometer measurements from Mariner gave no evidence of a magnetic field around that planet. This did not mean such a field was not present, but it did indicate that if Venus.had one, it was very weak—too weak to be detected by Mariner at a distance of 21,648 miles. Earth, on the other hand, has a strong magnetic field* which is the cause of the famous Van Allen radiation belts discovered by earlier earth-satellite experiments during the International Geophysical Year (1957-1958).

Preliminary results of the radiation-particle measurements were reviewed for a scientific meeting at Stanford University on December 28, 1962. The high-energy particle instrument on Mariner had been devised by Dr. H. R. Anderson of JPL and Dr. H. V. Neher of the California Institute of Technology. The low-energy (proton) device had been provided by L. A. Frank and Dr. J. A. Van Allen (of Van Allen-belt fame) of the State University of Iowa. One result of these tests confirmed the magnetometer information as to whether or not Venus has a magnetic field. At 21,000 miles, the instruments indicated no sudden rise in the presence of radioactive particles such as would have been present if a strong magnetic field had been there to trap them.

An important part of the experiments was measuring the intensity of cosmic radiation (radiation from outside the solar system) away from the disturbing effects of planets. Years of earth-based research has shown that variation in the amount of low-energy cosmic rays is systematic, covering an eleven-year cycle, and is connected with the sunspot cycle. If scientists can find out in more detail the relationship between these effects they will have gone a long way toward making possible successful manned space flight. Sunspots give rise to the sudden explosion from the sun's surface of solar flares, and the

---

* One of the units used to measure magnetic strength is the gamma. Earth has a magnetic field of 30,000 gammas at the equator and 50,000 gammas at the poles. By comparison, the Venus field, if it is present, is now estimated at only 5 gammas or less. Rough estimates of Jupiter's field, on the other hand, by means of radio impulses received from the planet, indicate it has a much stronger field than the earth.

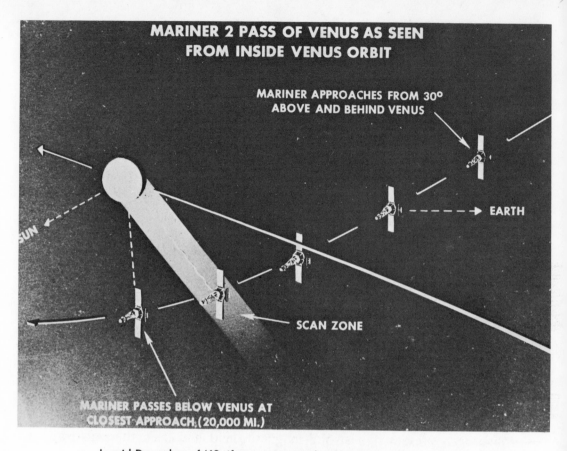

MARINER 2 PASS OF VENUS AS SEEN FROM INSIDE VENUS ORBIT

MARINER APPROACHES FROM 30°
ABOVE AND BEHIND VENUS

EARTH

SCAN ZONE

SUN

MARINER PASSES BELOW VENUS AT
CLOSEST APPROACH (20,000 MI.)

In mid-December of '62, if you were standing on the sun, this is what you would have seen. Mariner II approaches Venus from slightly above and between the planet and the sun. At 5:35 A.M. on December 14, orders from Goldstone are sent out to start the Venus scan sequence. For slightly over a half hour just before noon, Mariner II instruments scan the planet.

energy in these flares, which move rapidly out from the sun into space, is so tremendous that no human being could withstand them if caught in space during a solar storm. This makes its imperative that scientists develop an interplanetary weather warning system for the future so that manned spaceships can be warned in advance not to take off or remain in space when solar flares are due to happen.*

The geiger counters on Mariner II, it was reported, showed a

* For a discussion of sunspots and the International Year of the Quiet Sun, see Chapter 14.

68

cosmic-ray value of about 3.0 particles per-square-centimeter per second throughout the flight. Said Doctors Anderson and Frank, "The constancy of the cosmic ray intensity over the very great distance traveled by Mariner is a new and significant piece of information, but its real meaning will not become clear until we have repeated the experiment several times on space vehicles going out away from the sun as well as in toward it."

The instruments sent data to earth on one solar storm. The streams of high-energy particles from this flare, scientists told the meeting, began to reach Mariner II on October 23. The flare was observed on the sun about 9:42 A.M. and lasted until 10:45. So fast were the particles traveling, the Mariner instruments began recording an increase in particle count before the flare had disappeared. The ionization reading rose rapidly from 670 to 18,000 and remained at over 10,000 particles for six hours before declining slowly for several days afterward. The low-energy particles monitored by the geiger counters also rose from three to a peak of sixteen particles per-square-centimeter per second. Despite the intensity, this was a relatively minor storm that did not produce enough high-energy particles to have been dangerous to a man if he had been aboard the Mariner at that point.

Doctors Conway Snyder and Mrs. Marcia Neugebauer of JPL were also able to report on their measurements of solar plasma by December 28. Plasma, they noted, is an interplanetary gas flowing from the sun and called the solar wind. It is a mixture of bits of matter which have become ionized—that is, stripped of an electron so they are electrically charged. In our atmosphere, lightning is caused by the sudden discharge of an electrical charge on billions of ionized particles.

Solar plasma consists of a mixture of several different kinds of ions: hydrogen nuclei, helium nuclei and the nuclei of elements with heavier atomic weights. Such plasma was found all along Mariner's route, but the energy levels of the gas atoms were very low compared to the energy of cosmic-ray particles. Nonetheless, researchers reported, the number of solar-wind particles in this area is about a billion times the number of cosmic rays. Thus, when a storm erupts on the sun's surface, clouds of plasma are thrown out which suddenly drastically increase the speed of the solar wind. When such fast-moving clouds reach earth's atmosphere they disrupt various communication systems, from long-range radio to TV. This kind of information obtained from Mariner permits scientists to understand the solar-wind effects better and allows them to improve not only space communications but earth systems as well.

The auxiliary radar-bounce-test results were also reported to the Stanford meeting. Perhaps the most unusual information presented was that the signals indicated Venus was not only rotating very slowly, but it was actually rotating backward compared to earth's rotation. (Rotation is measured as a rotating body spreads or broadens the radar signal —that is, smears it—with the amount of spreading varying with the amount of rotation.) Because a rough surface scatters the radar signal, the radar beam was also directed across Venus' surface to obtain a general idea of its surface structure. This radar mapping indicated there is a surface feature on Venus that stands out, possibly a huge mountain—a finding that was verified by the information sent back by Mariner.

CHAPTER 9

A S 1962 FADED into 1963, space exploration interest shifted
to two main events. One was the progress of Russia's Mars
craft, the other the first report on Mariner's actual find-
ings about Venus. All seemed well with the former, though there was a
curious lack of information on one point: whether or not the all-
important mid-course maneuver had been attempted and completed.
On February 6, Tass reported, "Mars I station will have the following
astronomical coordinates on 6 February at nine o'clock in the morning
(Moscow time): 6 h. 35 m. right ascension, 32°52' declination. At that
time the station will be 52,018,000 kilometers from the earth. In the
next few days, the Mars I station, gradually shifting in space, is due to
pass from the constellation Auriga to the constellation Gemini."

In the meantime, the attention of many scientists in the United
States was also gradually shifting away from Venus and toward the
planet named for the Roman god of war. By late in 1962, a program for
the radar probing of Mars had begun in the United States.

The scientists worked and compared notes on the more than sixty-five million bits of information sent back by Mariner. The amount of data sent back is so vast that, even today, many scientists are still working at defining parts of it. But by the end of February 1963, enough data had been pieced together to give the waiting world some idea of what Mariner had found. On February 26, 1963, NASA and JPL called together a conference of reporters and editors from the major magazines, newspapers, TV and radio stations at which they held a question-and-answer session with the Mariner experimenters.

The two instruments placed on Mariner specifically for getting information about Venus were the infrared radiometer and the microwave radiometer. These sensitive devices could detect various types of radiation from the planet and its atmosphere, thereby permitting scientists to detect certain features of the environment. For instance, the infrared radiometer had special optical filters to filter light in two selected bands: 8 to 9 microns and 10 to 10.8 microns. Different elements emit light energy at different intensities. In the 8-9 micron region, no normal gases give off detectable infrared energy, and water vapor stops infrared beams in this band. So if the infrared radiometer were to be beamed where it could see directly to Venus' surface, the scientists would know there were breaks in Venus' cloud layer. In the 10-10.8 micron band, the top of any carbon dioxide column in the Venusian atmosphere would become visible to the infrared radiometer.

A microwave radiometer sends out signals called microwaves. Here, too, Mariner sent out signals at two different frequencies, one at a wavelength of 13.5 millimeters and one at 19 millimeters. At 13.5 mm., there is a water-vapor-absorption band. Thus, any return in this area would indicate the presence of a noticeable amount of water vapor in the atmosphere. The 19-mm. band isn't affected by water vapor and this radiometer could thus pierce Venus' clouds to reflect the planet's surface. The signals from this part of the instrument could then be analyzed to obtain temperature readings of the Venusian surface.

The key question, of course, was the planet's surface temperature. Was it really unbearably hot (for man)—several hundred degrees

Fahrenheit? Or were the scientific theories correct which stated that the great heat of Venus, as measured by some instruments from the earth, was due to the composition of that planet's clouds?

The scientists in charge of the microwave-radiometer experiment were Professor Barrett of the Massachusetts Institute of Technology and Dr. Douglas E. Jones of Brigham Young University. Dr. Jones told the February 26 conference that the instrument had made eighteen readings in the three scans of the planet. The actual readings given by the instrument had to be corrected for various factors, such as the effect of the atmosphere on signals reaching the microwave radiometer. But there could be only one conclusion from all considerations involved. Said Dr. Jones: the surface is indeed hot. His report stated:

"If we now take these numbers and assume a model, mathematically remove the absorption characteristics and also assume the emissivity* that the radar results predicted, we arrive at a fairly uniform temperature of about 800° F."

Certainly such a high temperature did not, at first glance, seem to promise much possibility of finding organic life on Venus. But Dr. Homer Newell of NASA told the press this was not necessarily so. "It is not likely that there is any life of the sort that we know. Biologists say it is possible that there may be lower-order life forms in the cooler upper atmosphere. They don't know that there are. . . . At the present time, the biologists are running experiments in earth's atmosphere (for instance, by sending up balloons to take samples) to try to find whether or not this is a sensible possibility."

What then, is the surface of Venus like with such an extreme temperature? Might the surface be one great molten mass, since 800° F. is above the melting point of many elements? From our earth environment, this would seem likely. And yet, as Dr. Eberhardt Rechtin, head of telecommunications for JPL, points out, the radar tests indicated otherwise. "I think from the radar data [received] that you could pretty well say it is not molten; because, if it were, we wouldn't get the roughness index that we see. We also wouldn't get these bright spots

* The emissivity of a surface is how much heat energy it gives off to its surroundings.

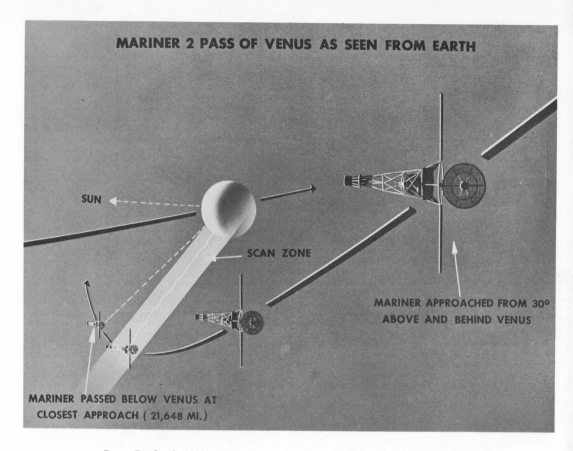

SUN

SCAN ZONE

MARINER APPROACHED FROM 30°
ABOVE AND BEHIND VENUS

MARINER PASSED BELOW VENUS AT
CLOSEST APPROACH (21,648 MI.)

From Earth, the Mariner II Venus pass would look like this. Once past Venus, Mariner's radios send information for a few weeks, then fall silent.

[indicating mountains] and other variations. . . . The measurements, instead, are more suggestive of sand and dust than they are at least, of many molten things."

And what about the cloud layer—was it also as hot as the surface? And was it, as many scientists thought, composed primarily of carbon dioxide? The instrument designed to give the first-possible direct answers to these questions was the infrared radiometer, provided by Drs. L. D. Kaplan of JPL, Gerry Neugebauer of JPL and Cal Tech, and Carl Sagan of the University of California at Berkeley. The information, stated Dr. Kaplan, indicated that the cloud cover was indeed very thick, with the base of the clouds at an altitude of about forty-five miles above Venus' surface and the cloud tops at the sixty-mile altitude. Though there might be breaks in the clouds, actually the Mariner information did not indicate anything to prove these breaks existed. It is the thickness of these clouds, scientists believe, that causes a "greenhouse effect," resulting in the very high temperatures on the planet's surface.

The readings seemed quite constant, Dr. Kaplan said, except for one variation. At one point along the terminator (the line dividing the planet in half) and its southern end, the temperature appeared to be about twenty degrees cooler. Said Kaplan: "One obvious interpretation is that the clouds at this point are locally higher. This would seem to indicate some unusual surface feature—perhaps a huge mountain—a possibility also indicated by the radar-bounce tests." The cloud temperatures, the instruments showed, ranged from about 200° F. at the base of the clouds to from —30 to —70° F. at the cloud tops. (The cloud tops were about —30° F. at the center of Venus and about —60 to —70° F. at the edges of the planet.)

Little carbon dioxide was apparently present above the cloud tops, bearing out the theory of their being very thick and dense. The temperature at the cloud base, though, was too high, said Dr. Kaplan, for the presence of carbon dioxide. There had to be something else there—a substance that would condense, be present in fairly small quantities, and not be detectable from earth-based spectrographic measurements. The most likely substance in this case, it was decided, would be oil or smog. The information also indicated that, to have a greenhouse effect causing the high surface temperature, a great deal of carbon dioxide was probably in the atmosphere below the cloud bank. The atmospheric pressure, scientists also figured out, is probably very high—about twenty times that of earth.

This, then, was man's first detailed picture of Venus. But this first intriguing peek provided only the merest glimpse at the true nature of that planet. In addition, it posed some brand new questions, whose answers could be obtained only by other Venus probes of future Project Mariners or their successors.

CHAPTER 10

T HE NEXT Venus round, though, would have to wait. The NASA and JPL Mariner people turned their gaze to the proximity of Mars to earth in 1964. The Russian space probe which was due to reach the vicinity of Mars in June 1963, was considered a definite scientific gain. The Russian probe was known to be equipped to take TV pictures of the planet. Similar equipment on the Mariner fly-by in 1965 (a launch in late 1964 would bring Mariner to Mars in mid-1965) would provide a rare opportunity to compare information from two different sources. In this instance, the Russian probe and the Mariner would pass by Mars on different trajectories, with different instruments designed to garner different facts. Comparing the TV pictures from the two would then give a double check on the surface variations of the planet.

However, even as the first thoughts were given to the next Mariner mission, it became obvious that something had gone wrong with the

Russian flight. U.S. scientists were puzzled by the fact that no mention had been made of a mid-course maneuver. Plans for the maneuver had been revealed in early dispatches from Tass. Then, as the early months of 1963 passed, the Tass bulletins about Mars I's position suddenly ceased. There was silence for quite some time. Finally, though, word was issued that the communications system on the spacecraft had failed. Contact had been lost and the craft would drift silently past the planet.

The evidence seemed to point to a double failure: first, of the mid-course maneuver, second, of the radio transmitter. Even if Mars I had maintained contact with earth under these circumstances, it would probably have been too far from the planet to make meaningful observations.

All this again stressed the difficulty of any mission's succeeding in these first pioneering days of space exploration. The Mars mission would not have the high-temperature dangers of the Venus flight, since the probe vehicle would be going away from the sun. But the temperature problem would still be there—heat still had to be balanced properly and, in this case, the chance of temperatures becoming too cold for proper equipment operation had to be considered. Thermal considerations were just one facet of the problem—there were many other factors as well that complicated the Mars attempt.

As Dan Schneiderman, the Mariner Spacecraft Systems Manager, states: "Mariner II gave us at JPL confidence in our methods and abilities. After all, nobody before had ever done this job but us. We were and still are the experts. But we knew we were only on the threshold of a partly opened door. The trip past Venus had been tough —and it took only less than four months. The one to Mars, though, would be more than twice as long in elapsed time, meaning twice as much time for something to fail in the complex equipment aboard.

"We had learned much from Mariner II. Our thermal-control people went right back into careful testing based on the new temperature information learned from the Venus shot. They spent many hours finding the reasons for the differences between the information

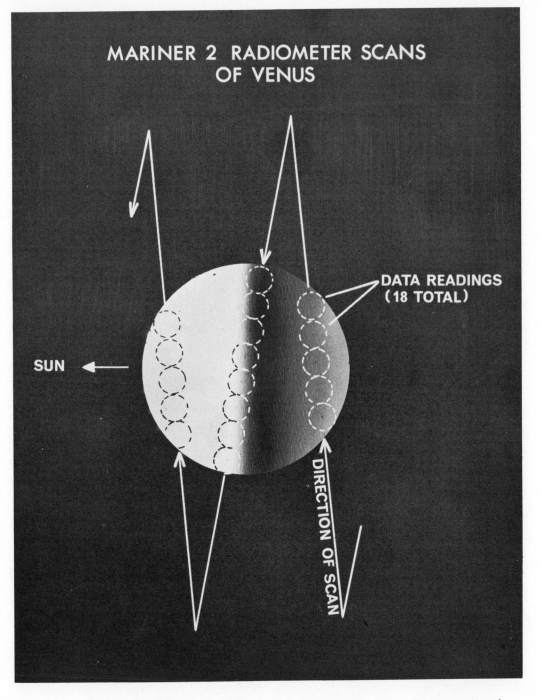

Up and down, during the half-hour Venus pass, Mariner II's radiometer scanned the planet. From the spacecraft, 18 separate data points are radioed back to Earth.

we got from preflight tests and the way Mariner II actually performed. By mid-1963 we felt we knew the temperatures to be met on a Mars shot, and how to plan for them. We felt sure of the answers to many other obstacles, too. But we still could not know if what we expected was correct until the spacecraft sent back the confirming information we lacked. And then it might be too late to do anything about it."

The design steps to be followed in developing the Mars craft (designated Mariner C) were, in many ways, basically a repeat of those for Mariner II: months of conferences among all types of specialists, meeting after meeting to review all the information about Mars and decide what shape the new vehicle should take. The scientists would be asked for suggestions for experiments and more meetings would be needed to decide which ones should finally be adopted. Then would come the completion by the engineers of the detailed drawings for Mariner C and the production of the first hardware.

But there was an added problem that now had to be solved. This involved the human equation. The demands of Mariner II had been more exhausting than anyone could have predicted. As Tom Bilbo emphasizes, "Some kind of rehabilitation had to be done on almost all of those who took part in the Mariner II program. They were all over-worked and the tensions had stretched their nerves thin. Remember, there were no days off for us in the three and a half months of the Venus voyage. This kind of tension is not alleviated merely by a couple of nights' sleep."

The NASA and JPL veterans could not, therefore, just plunge into the details of the Mars assignment. For several months they had to do less taxing things, like catching up with their paperwork and, in turn, going on vacations that were true releases. The Mariner C program managers had to make sure there would be far more trained people ready to work on the new task. In addition, a special analysis would have to be made of the whole flight-control operation to try to take as many burdens off human shoulders as possible. A major answer to this was improved equipment. In particular, the ground-based com-

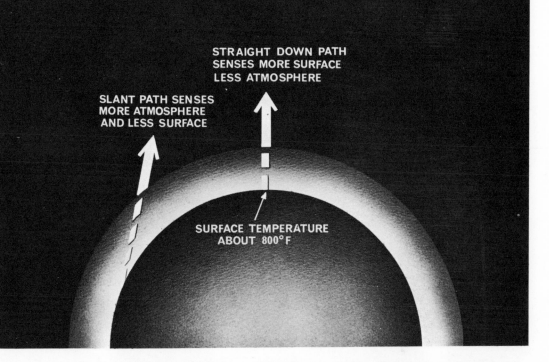

MARINER 2 MICROWAVE TEMPERATURE STUDY OF THE
VENUS ATMOSPHERE AND SURFACE

STRAIGHT DOWN PATH
SENSES MORE SURFACE
LESS ATMOSPHERE

SLANT PATH SENSES
MORE ATMOSPHERE
AND LESS SURFACE

SURFACE TEMPERATURE
ABOUT 800°F

Venus surface temperature was measured by the Mariner microwave radiometer. Readings had to be corrected for the angle at which they were taken
relative to the atmosphere. Final value, scientists stated, was an average surface
temperature of 800 degrees F.

puters would have to be designed to do more of the work than they had
done before.

In an effort to streamline the planning and staffing approach to
the Mars program, JPL set up a study team to inspect complex operations in the business world and in such military setups as the Strategic
Air Command. Curiously enough, the first industry to be studied was
electric power, the system that supplies the electricity to light our homes
and run our factories. This industry runs vast networks of equipment

with only a few men. For instance, at the steam-generating plant, huge boilers make steam that drives turbines which rotate electric generators that deliver electricity to cities through copper or aluminum wires.

In the various plants there are hundreds of dials, valves and pipes, all monitored by only a handful of employees.

The few men who make up the entire work force do not have to be highly trained college graduates. They do have to be naturally intelligent and be able to read dials correctly. These men have several telephone numbers to call if the dials indicate anything unusual or dangerous. The numbers belong to the electric company's top-flight engineers or managers who can take charge in any moment of danger, or difficulty.

The operations of a Strategic Air Command post and a Nike missile base were also examined. Both have certain characteristics in common. Their day-to-day operations can become deadly dull. The people running them have daily checking tasks. Some are more demanding than others. In general, however, a great deal of time is spent just in waiting for something to happen. (In this case, of course, waiting is to be preferred. As long as they are kept waiting it means there will be no shooting.) But waiting is tedious. The inactivity of an isolated station can dull the intellect and drive high-strung people to distraction.

The staff for the Mars probe and those following it had to be composed of people who were constitutionally suited to withstand boredom, but who were also able to spring to full activity when necessary. The way to keep such a staff in top form is to relieve it at frequent intervals, but without endangering the project.

With this in mind, JPL researchers looked at the way the Venus mission had been run and compared it with operations in the electric power plant, SAC and Nike bases and other similar enterprises. Ways were then found for adding special equipment to certain jobs and for figuring out routines that would permit using junior engineers and other trainees for more of the routine work.

The difficulty here was that, even with a larger staff of experts, there would still be a limit to the number of top-level people who could be found for such a project. Admittedly, the juniors would not have the required experience or sufficient confidence in themselves to function as well as the top-level first team. But, notes Operations Director Tom Bilbo, "If a man can read a danger signal, which he can be quickly taught to do, and he knows the right telephone numbers in order to call the experts who can make decisions, the first team need not be in there working under tension around the clock for more than half a year."

Thus, a special system of training was devised to acquaint the junior engineer with the alarm limits for key parts of the Mars-probe system. This, in turn, required that the spacecraft designers consider how to modify the various signals sent from the craft to provide better, more positive alarm limits. For instance, the designers had to calculate what combinations of effects would begin to cause different systems to work improperly. They had to figure out ways to catch such effects much further in advance. That way, when a warning alarm was given, there would be time for a junior engineer to summon help and for that help to arrive in time to make the needed correction.

CHAPTER 11

A S THE design engineers worked on testing and other space-craft problems, and the flight-control group prepared to add new staff members, NASA and JPL scientists started reviewing what was known about Mars. Unlike Venus, it was quite a bit. This is because it is possible to see Mars' surface directly, for Mars is not completely covered with thick clouds as is Venus. Though Mars does have some cloud formations, generally they are relatively small and do not obstruct much of our view of the planet. The amount of surface detail we can note on Mars from earth is second in quantity only to that of the moon. The fourth planet out from the sun, Mars at its closest approaches the earth at a distance of about 35,000,000 miles and at its farthest about 240,000,000 miles.

The first look at Mars from earth was made over three centuries ago. In 1610, the great Italian astronomer Galileo Galilei was the first man to view it through a telescope. Christian Huygens, a Dutchman, in

1659, and Robert Hooke, an Englishman, in 1660, made the first sketches of the Martian surface and calculated many of the properties of the planet. Hooke, for instance, stated that the planet made one complete rotation every twenty-four hours, a calculation very close to that accepted today. As time went on, more and more powerful telescopes and other sensitive instruments led to new discoveries. In 1877, an American, Asaph Hall, found that Mars actually had two satellites. (There have been recent Russian suggestions that at least one of these satellites acts as if it had originally been made by some intelligent being, rather than being a natural object.) Its two satellites orbit at different heights above Mars, one fairly close to the surface and one much farther out. Hall named the inner one Phobos and the outer one Deimos. He took these names from the horses in Greek mythology which pulled the chariot of the god Mars. Phobos is so close to Mars and its orbit is so fast that, to someone standing on that planet's surface, it would seem to rise in the west and set in the east not once but three times in one day. Deimos moves much more slowly than Phobos; therefore, two days would go by between its rising and setting. The diameter of Deimos is estimated to be about ten miles and that of Phobos from fourteen to eighteen miles. Thus, the satellites are very small as compared to the accepted estimate of Mars' diameter, about 4,190 miles.

In the year 1877, at the same time as Asaph Hall's discovery of Mars' two satellites, the interest of both the public and the scientific community was also aroused by speculation over the nature of the Martian "canals." These canals are long, thin, straight lines that appear to crisscross the planet. A few of them have been observed for hundreds of years, but the existence of many more was reported by the Italian astronomer G. V. Schiaparelli in 1877, who gave them the Italian name *canali.*

The canals are still the subject of great controversy. Many astronomers in the late 1800's said they never saw the markings noted by Schiaparelli. Some people who believed him to be right thought the canals were evidence that a form of highly intelligent beings had once inhabited or perhaps still inhabit Mars. Since the scientific measurements of the planet indicate the planet's atmosphere cannot support life as we know it, some individuals have proposed the thesis that a well-developed civilization built these works ages ago and then died out as Mars slowly lost its atmosphere. Of course, there is also the possibility that a form of life exists on Mars which is different from that on earth.

The feeling of many scientists in recent years is that the canal markings are there, all right, but the interplanetary distance involved and the tricks that light sometimes plays make it impossible to make them out exactly. These researchers also feel that these are natural markings. Schiaparelli himself pointed out that even though geometrical markings are generally associated with man-made things, there is proof that such markings can occur naturally. Saturn's rings, he noted, are regular geometric shapes and seashells often contain perfect geometric patterns. It has also been observed that systems of streaks sometimes seem to radiate out from craters on the moon, yet no one suggests these are made by living beings.

During the Mars "great opposition"* in 1956, Russian astronomers in the Kharkov Observatory noted the disappearance of bright spots and stripes on one part of the surface and the appearance of a bright wide canal in their place. Normally, reported astronomer N. P. Barabeshev, only six canals are observed, "but some observers have reported seeing a larger number."

There is still a great deal of scientific dispute over the actual existence of these linear markings. The well-known astronomer G. P. Kuiper, of the University of Arizona, said at the Ninth Lunar and Planetary Colloquium** in November 1960:

"Even though one observes Mars under good conditions, one cannot be certain of having a geometric system of narrow straight lines. The surface of the planet is covered with complex detail and certainly

---

* The great opposition—or closest approach of Mars to earth—occurs once every fifteen to seventeen years. The next great opposition will come again in 1971.
** The Colloquium is an informal get-together of scientists interested in the solar system, including most of the major researchers in this field from NASA and JPL.

under limited resolution* some of these features may have a linear appearance. The history of the Mars canals is a rather unfortunate one in that it has hindered our study of the planet's surface—but perhaps it has stimulated interest as well.

"I would like to point out [though] that the observations by E. E. Barnard of Lick Observatory in the 1890's and E. M. Antoniadi in 1909, and the more recent observations of the last oppositions [in the 1950's] are all in agreement that there is no geometric structure on Mars."

Are there canals or not? The final answer depends on Mariner C and the programs which follow it.

---

* Resolution means the ability of an instrument, such as a telescope, to resolve—that is, make sharp and unblurred—a view of an area on an astral body.

CHAPTER 12

A S SEEN through a telescope, the over-all appearance of
Mars' surface is deep yellow or orange. Alternating with
these areas are "dark" portions that seem to be bluish-
green in color. At the planet's poles are large white polar caps. It should
be stressed that the planet only *seems* to have these colors. Its atmosphere plus the long distance the light must travel to reach earth distort
the colorations viewed; therefore, they are probably different from what
man sees. As scientist C. Sagan of the University of California at
Berkeley has pointed out, the color of the bluish-green areas "is not
green, but predominantly gray, with perhaps a few other colors inter-
spersed which are very difficult to distinguish."

The blue-green color of the dark areas on Mars originally led to
the conclusion that these were bodies of water. Hence, they were called
maria, or oceans. But the many photographs and other observations
made of Mars in recent decades indicate the dark areas change color

with the seasons. They change from blue-green to yellow and, as first reported by the American astronomer Percival Lowell in 1903-1905, from green to chocolate brown. Some scientific observers still believe that several of the dark areas are lakes or small bodies of water. But it is also agreed that the drastic color changes generally rule out the idea of water masses in the darkest regions. A more likely answer is that some form of plant life exists on Mars that changes colors with the seasons.

On one point there is complete agreement: Mars does have polar caps that expand and shrink with the seasons. (Russian astronomer Barabeshev said his calculations indicated the polar caps are "located at some distance from rather than on the planet's surface.") Their composition is definitely some form of water, either ice or frost. Detailed observations of the caps were made by French scientists at the Paris observatory during the great opposition (the close approach of Mars to earth) in 1956 and again in 1958. As A. Dollfus of the Paris observatory told the 1960 Planetary Colloquium, a number of small cloud formations were seen over the polar region.

An important outcome of these observations was the indication that there might be mountains or hills in the polar areas. In the past, it was theorized that the planet's surface was very regular, with relatively few elevated areas. However, notes Dollfus, constant watching of the cloud shadows which stood out well against the polar-cap background indicated the clouds remained fixed in place for several days at a time. This, he notes, might be proof of the existence of mountains, or at least hills, on Mars' surface, since such formations would tend to keep the clouds from moving.

Another mystery of the planet observed by Dollfus and his co-workers was the yellow veil that spread across the Martian surface during much of the 1956 period. Special instruments were used to discover the properties of this veil. The Dollfus group tried to simulate the Mars environment in the laboratory. Then they placed various materials in this artificial environment to see if one would produce something like the yellow veil they had observed through the telescope. It was

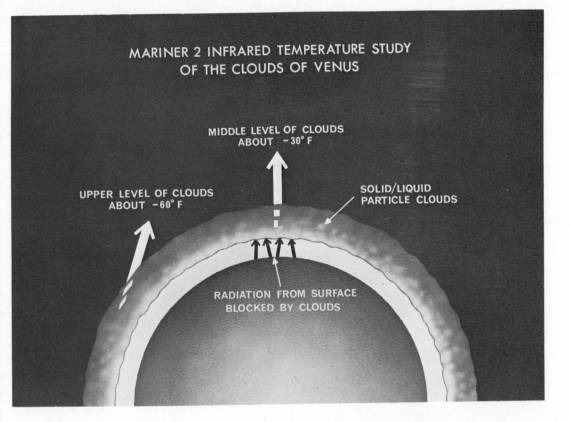

MARINER 2 INFRARED TEMPERATURE STUDY
OF THE CLOUDS OF VENUS

MIDDLE LEVEL OF CLOUDS
ABOUT −30° F

UPPER LEVEL OF CLOUDS
ABOUT −60° F

SOLID/LIQUID
PARTICLE CLOUDS

RADIATION FROM SURFACE
BLOCKED BY CLOUDS

Venus cloud study results from Mariner's infrared radiometer are shown in this NASA-JPL sketch.

thought the veil might be dust clouds, but the introduction of dust into the experiment did not produce a veil. Other materials were tried in turn, but the one which seemed to have the closest resemblance to the veil was *cigarette smoke,* or possibly smog!

As the time for the U.S. earth-probe exploration of Mars drew closer, scientists throughout the world were setting up models of Mars' atmosphere to study other possible answers to the planet's riddles. In particular, efforts were made to see whether life forms known on earth could survive there. As Dr. Rainer Berger of Lockheed-California, said, "Of all the planets, Mars, which has water and a surface temperature reaching up to sixty degrees, has the best climate to sustain life, and scorching Venus [has] one of the worst." Despite this encouraging viewpoint, Dr. Berger's research, as well as that of other laboratory experimenters, indicates that the existence of life on Mars would rule out the possibility of any form higher than microorganisms (such as bacteria) or elementary plants.

This feeling is based on the most recent estimates of temperature and atmospheric pressure on the planet. Until recently, long-distance measurements from earth indicated the Martian atmosphere had a pressure about one-tenth that of earth. In the early 1960's, more accurate measurements showed Mars' surface pressure to be between 15 and 20 millibars against a value for earth of 700-720 millibars. Therefore, the atmospheric pressure on Mars is now believed to be less than

One of the first parts to be built for the Mariner Mars craft was the solar panel assembly. Here an engineer at Ryan Aeronautical Corp. checks over a panel structure. The panel is held in place by a special tubular production jig.

a thirtieth of earth's. In earth's atmosphere, when a man ascends in a plane or a balloon to an altitude of over 15,000 feet, he must have special equipment—an oxygen mask or a pressurized cabin—even though the pressure outside is still many times that of Mars' surface. Many scientists therefore estimate it would be almost impossible for any form of intelligent animal life to exist in the Martian "air."

However, this may not be too conclusive. As NASA researchers point out, most biologists formerly maintained that life could not exist in the depths of the ocean. These biologists incorrectly felt that the great drop in atmospheric pressure made it next to impossible for life to exist at places such as the tops of the highest mountains. They therefore maintained that the tremendous pressures at the ocean bottoms would also prevent the sustenance of higher forms of animal life. In the 1960's, however, these theories were disproved when the famous bathyscaphe explored the very deepest part of earth's ocean (35,700 feet down) and found fish swimming on the bottom.

Combined with the Martian low atmospheric pressure, though, is a temperature range that also seems opposed to the support of higher forms of life. Recent observations have indicated a more extreme range than was suggested by earlier research.*

Richard Young of NASA Ames, in charge of work on simulation of Mars' environment, reports, the night temperature on Mars seems to have a year-round average of —100° Centigrade. The most favorable conditions for the fostering of life, he states, is at the Martian equator, where the temperature seems to fluctuate from —100° C. to +30° C. during the summer. For four to four and a half hours at midday in that season the temperature stays reasonably above zero. Based on what we know about life on earth, he notes, it would seem unlikely mammals could survive under such conditions.

However, in special test chambers at Ames Laboratory, Moffett Field, California, Mr. Young's group has shown that some earth bac-

* Many things still can only be guessed at in figuring out Martian temperatures from observations made on earth. Even the most recent measurements may be no more correct than those taken a few years ago. In the long run, we will not know what Mars is really like until we get there.

teria could survive under the Martian equatorial climate. And if water were available, these bacteria could even grow and thrive. Earth-based instruments can detect very little water on Mars other than at the polar caps. NASA researchers feel, however, water might be present elsewhere in the form of a thin permafrost layer not detectable by our astronomical instruments. Young's group therefore tried to duplicate the Martian environment with a model whose polar caps and surface coloration would change with the same seasonal relation we are able to observe on Mars through the telescope. When this was accomplished, the results did show that a thin frost layer formed on the model's surface in areas other than the polar caps. Therefore, there might be more water on Mars than we had originally suspected, possibly existing in combination with various chemicals.

It is known that Mars has an atmosphere of gases surrounding it. Exactly what these gases are is still being debated. One of the problems is that the method used to analyze materials on another planet involves spectroscopic breakdown of the light reflected by the planet. Each element, such as oxygen, hydrogen, etc., can be identified by its characteristic line pattern on the spectroscope.* However, the light from Mars must reach us through our own atmosphere—at least until such time as the first orbiting astronomical observatories are placed in space. This means that the spectroscopic lines for Martian elements which are also found in earth's atmosphere are confused with those of our own atmosphere. That is, scientists cannot be sure that a Mars-reflected light pattern for oxygen is not just an observation of oxygen in earth's atmosphere. In such a case, they might wrongly think Mars' atmosphere contained oxygen when it really contains little or none at all.

But some rough conclusions have been drawn with the aid of complex mathematical analyses. The major difficulty is that different scientists have reached entirely different conclusions. Some have stated the Martian atmosphere contains much water vapor and some oxygen. Recent spectrum studies by the Mt. Wilson Observatory indicate that

* See Chapter 4 for further discussion of the spectroscope.

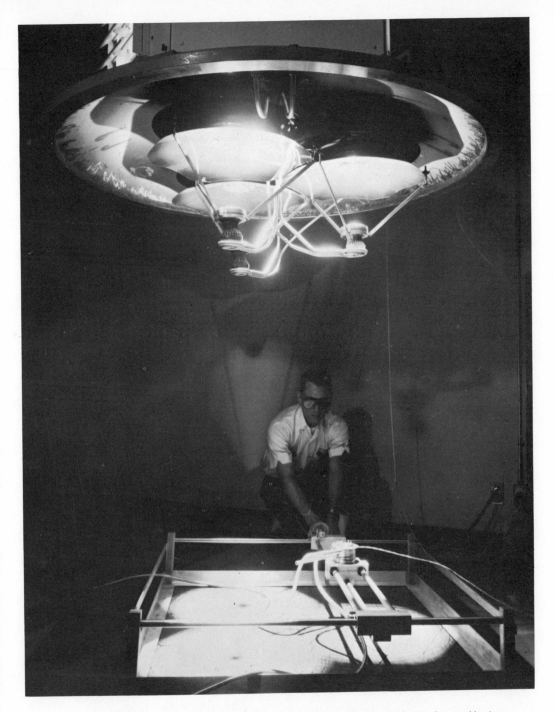

Among the advanced solar simulation chambers being built for future Mariner, Voyager and similar programs is the huge facility at NASA Goddard Space Flight Center. Very powerful lamp systems, such as these, were developed for duplicating sunlight by Minneapolis-Honeywell Corporation.

Mars' atmosphere has almost no oxygen and water vapor. The argument for the existence of water vapor and perhaps rainstorms is strong, however, because of the clouds and changes in the polar caps that are observed. There is always a chance, though, that the clouds and polar caps are made of something other than water. Some carbon dioxide has definitely been detected in Mars' atmosphere. Scientists cannot be sure whether there is a lot or a little. The best estimate up to 1963 was that the Mars atmosphere is made up of ninety-four percent nitrogen, two percent carbon dioxide, four percent argon and with perhaps minor traces of water vapor, oxygen, neon, xenon and krypton.

The foregoing are some of the conflicting theories about Mars. We seem to know a lot about the planet; and yet it is not much at all. For every surmise a scientist can make based on information at hand, another scientist can come up with a radically different idea. Even for the moon, as NASA Administrator James Webb once pointed out, "there are as many theories about what the lunar surface is made of as there are researchers studying the problem."

CHAPTER 13

T HE VOYAGE of the Mariner C and its successors would
finally begin to give scientists hard and accurate facts on
which to base their Martian studies. From these studies
could come the groundwork needed to send manned missions safely to
other space bodies. This is extremely important in the case of Mars, for
there is much evidence to suggest that that planet is similar enough to
earth to support our expeditions. It might even be possible someday to
raise giant glassed-in cities on Mars.

Many leading scientists and engineers therefore believe Mars may
provide man with one of the greatest bonanzas in history. Chester Haig,
Jr., of the Advanced Design department of McDonnell Aircraft (build-
ers of project Gemini and Mercury capsules), made the following
statement to the Interplanetary Missions Conference in January 1963:
"Although it is impossible to predict the exact nature of the scientific
knowledge that will be gained from the exploration of Mars, there is

reason to believe it will be very large. Possibly the exploration of Mars will result in a greater scientific pay-off than any other scientific project that we might undertake in the foreseeable future."

Throughout 1963, the problems and possible solutions to future exploration of the planets were reviewed at one conference after another. Most of these solutions emphasized dependence on Mariner-type missions for the later manned voyages they would lead to. At the NASA-sponsored seminar on Manned Planetary Mission Technology held in Cleveland in late May, E. F. Lally of JPL discussed a four-man mission to Mars. This would be based on first landing an unmanned vehicle on the Martian moon Phobos. The craft would contain a payload of extra fuel for the return flight to earth, a laboratory and two spacecraft. Later on, he stated, astronauts would land on Phobos and use the two spacecraft to descend to Mars' surface.

Many other papers at this and succeeding meetings continued to emphasize the great hopes scientists and engineers hold for Mars studies. In June 1963, the first major meeting exclusively devoted to Mars was held. It was called the Symposium of the Exploration of Mars. The wide range of interest in the subject was shown by the many technical societies sponsoring the conference. Included were: the American Astronomical Society, the American Astronautical Society, the American Institute of Biological Sciences, the American Institute of Aeronautics and Astronautics (AIAA) and the National Aeronautics and Space Administration (NASA). Still another meeting on interplanetary missions was sponsored in October by the AIAA. At these gatherings, scientists compared notes on many important aspects of the Mars mission. Their discussions ranged from trajectories to communications, spacecraft design, life sciences and the scientific information which should be obtained from manned and unmanned exploration.

As the scientists discussed the problems involved, JPL engineers were firming some of the details for the Mariner Mars mission. It was decided that the launch vehicle should be the newer Atlas D-Agena D combination. The Agena D, an improved version of the Agena B upper-

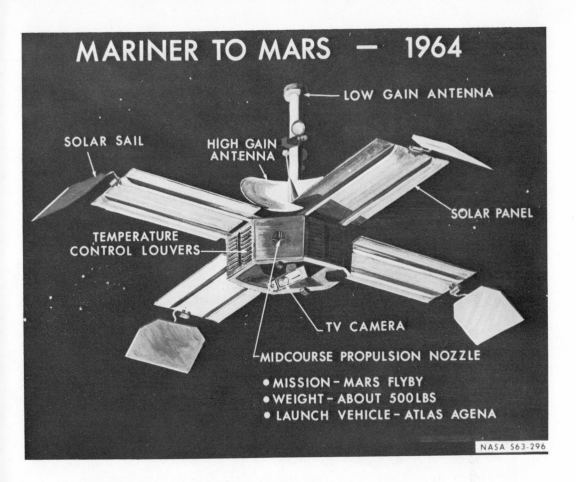

MARINER TO MARS — 1964

LOW GAIN ANTENNA

SOLAR SAIL

HIGH GAIN ANTENNA

SOLAR PANEL

TEMPERATURE CONTROL LOUVERS

TV CAMERA

MIDCOURSE PROPULSION NOZZLE

- MISSION — MARS FLYBY
- WEIGHT — ABOUT 500 LBS
- LAUNCH VEHICLE — ATLAS AGENA

NASA S63-296

stage rocket booster used with Mariner II, would provide enough extra thrust to permit a much heavier Mariner C. Now, instead of the 447 pounds of Mariner II, JPL engineers could figure on a total spacecraft weight of six hundred pounds. Of this total, some sixty pounds of instruments could be included, a gain of over thirty percent in payload capacity compared to the Venus flight. The goal of the program was to launch the probe sometime between November 12 and 26, 1964, but preferably on November 19, so that it would pass within about 13,500 miles of Mars about seven and one-half months later. (Though the 13,500-mile distance was the design goal, scientists estimated useful information could be gained about Mars at any distance up to 125,000 miles from its surface.)

During this fifteen-day period in November 1964, the relationship of earth to Mars was such that it would require a minimum amount of energy to make the voyage. The November 19 launch date called for the least amount of energy of all. The less energy and fuel weight needed to make the journey, of course, the bigger the payload could be.

The increased weight of Mariner C gave the engineers more leeway in making their designs productive and reliable. Gaining a greater vehicle weight was a must. This was particularly true of spacecraft power. On a voyage to Mars, the vehicle goes away from the sun. If solar cells are used to convert sunlight into electrical energy, more solar cells are then needed, since the sun's rays are weaker in the outer areas of space. To meet this need, engineers decided to use four solar panels instead of the two on Mariner II. Each Mariner C panel would have a surface area of seventy square feet.

As with Mariner II, the solar-cell panels were designed to be held in a folded position during launch with explosive pins used to release the panels once Mariner C was ready for its space trip. This time, however, something new was added to the ends of the panels in the form of four large solar vanes to help keep the craft balanced in space. As satellite flights have shown, the steady stream of plasma from the sun (the so-called solar wind) can cause sufficient pressure on a surface to make it shift direction because in space there is no air to oppose the motion of a body. A slight amount of pressure on one side of the vehicle, if not offset on the other, can therefore cause the craft to rotate in position.

This balancing, can also be done with gas jets. On Mariner II, such jets were used both to move the craft for desired maneuvers and to balance out any sun-pressure effects. However, the more a gas-jet system must be used, the more gas must be stored on board—and the more gas-storage space that is required, the greater the weight of this maneuvering system and the less weight allowed for instruments. This was even more of a potential problem on Mariner C than on Mariner II, due to the much longer time it would take to get to Mars.

Use of the solar vanes was made possible by information gains from the Venus probe. These vanes could not be used on Mariner II because at that time the engineers didn't have enough information about the nature of the solar wind to know how to design the vane system. They needed a better idea of the strength of the plasma, whether it "blew" regularly or not and what it was made of. Mariner II provided such data.

On Mariner Mars, solar-wind sensors are used to send information on solar pressure to the vehicle's computer. This computer then sends signals to small actuators to turn the vanes and maintain proper balance. Gas jets are still needed for major maneuvers, but the passive vane system could be used for all other balancing operations.

On the new Mariner all electronic equipment (batteries, etc.) is still stored in the main spacecraft bus. In this case, the bus was made octagonal (eight-sided) rather than hexagonal (six-sided). The eight equipment bays of this design provided a storage volume of about 4.65 cubic feet, fifty-five percent more room than was available on Mariner II. Instead of installing the complex tubular structure on top of the bus, as they did on Mariner II, JPL engineers used a six-foot tube with a diameter of four inches with a low-gain antenna located on its top.

Also, the high-gain antenna was relocated to the top of the bus instead of underneath it. For most of the journey, signals from earth to the vehicle would be picked up by the low-gain antenna. During the last third of the trip, the central computer was to switch over to the more powerful high-gain antenna. While the craft was passing close to Mars' surface, the high-gain antenna was to be pointed back to earth to relay information on the experiments.

As with Mariner II, a sun-sensor system was to be used to line up Mariner C along its flight path. The new craft, however, would not use the sun and the earth as references; the sun and the bright star Canopus were selected this time. By making shadow graphs of the spacecraft course and placing the charts over maps of the heavens, it could be found what the sensors would see as the ship changed position. Similar charts were made for the different locations of the sensors on the spacecraft. Taking into consideration the instrument positions and

Both Atlas and Centaur vehicles are produced by Astronautics Div. of General Dynamics Corp. Here a Centaur is shown in between two Atlases on the Astronautics production line in San Diego, Calif. The rings shown on the outsides of the missiles are simply supports to keep the thin-gauge steel skins from buckling during assembly. Afterward, the rings are removed. The Atlas-Centaur's first mission at present is to send the Surveyor landing probe to the moon. In later years, though, an Atlas-Centaur is slated to launch much larger Mariner vehicles. Then, after Centaur is mated to a still more powerful booster than the Atlas, such as the Saturn, it will send Voyager spacecraft to orbit and land on Mars and/or Venus.

other structural requirements, it was then possible to combine the best sensor position with the most efficient star target. The Mariner C scientists therefore decided Canopus would provide the best sensor target for this mission, since it is the brightest star in the southern sky.

The mid-course guidance engine design was also improved. The engine still would produce only about fifty pounds of thrust. But now, instead of firing only once, the increased weight of Mariner C permitted the carrying of additional fuel and the engine could fire twice. If the first mid-course maneuver attempt did not line the ship up correctly, the ground controllers would then have a second chance.

With one system after another, the engineers tried to apply what they had learned from the earlier flight to make the next one more accurate. It is this learning from previous experience that has made successful rocket launches commonplace where once, not too many years ago, our missile and space program suffered one failure after another. In the future, spaceships will be able to make as many mid-course maneuvers as necessary and still end up on the right road to the planets.

CHAPTER 14

A S THE engineers designed, the Mariner C scientists labored to perfect their experiments. The prime target of the Mars mission was to find out if there really was life on the planet. The equipment array was planned to include data-gathering instruments not sent on the Venus probe; initially these included a TV camera and an infrared spectrometer. The TV camera would relay pictures of the Martian surface to earth while the infrared detector would send along an analysis indicating what kind of matter the TV camera was looking at.

The infrared spectrometer is an excellent tool for such measurements. Most materials and, as far as is known, all living things, give off heat energy in the form of infrared radiation, different materials giving off different intensities. When a particular radiation intensity is observed, it is then known that a certain material is present.

As an example of the uses of infrared studies on our own planet, we might point out such everyday pursuits as agriculture, where it is applied to the health of trees. It may not be possible to find a diseased tree in an orchard with the naked eye; yet, if the tree is not destroyed quickly, it can soon infect the healthy trees all around it. When an infrared picture is taken of the orchard from the air, the diseased trees stand out immediately as a different shade of gray from the rest. The owner can then chop down the sick trees and guard the health of his orchard. The difference in infrared registration is caused by the fact that the diseased trees have slightly higher temperatures than the healthy trees—just as sick people have higher temperatures than healthy people. A higher temperature results in a change in the strength of infrared energy given off by the trees, hence the different color in the picture.

Unfortunately, as the Mariner '64 design proceeded, JPL found the infrared experiment would weigh too much to be included. It was decided to use only the TV for direct Mars observations. However, for the next Mariner Mars flights in 1966, the infrared instrument was considered a must. (By 1966, the Centaur upper stage will be ready, permitting a Mariner weight of over 1000 pounds.)

Observations along the way in interplanetary space would also be as important as they were on the Venus voyage. Now that a great deal of information had been gained on the charged particles and dust between Venus and the earth, scientists were eager to see how things looked in the direction away from the sun. It was expected that the amounts and nature of matter would follow a general pattern from the sun to the farthest reaches of the solar system. Still, there was always the chance of some unexpected discovery, such as a greater number of cosmic particles might be found. In either case, gaining more measurements on previously unexplored regions would help to give man a better knowledge of how the universe worked.

The same basic type of experiment instruments were designed for the Mariner C interplanetary voyage as had been used on Mariner II. These included solar-plasma detectors, an ion chamber, cosmic ray counters and a magnetometer. The timing of the Mars opposition gave Mariner C a further important role in a new and exciting scientific effort that had enlisted the services of scientists throughout the world. This was the project known as the International Year of the Quiet Sun.

The success of the International Geophysical Year, 1957-1958,

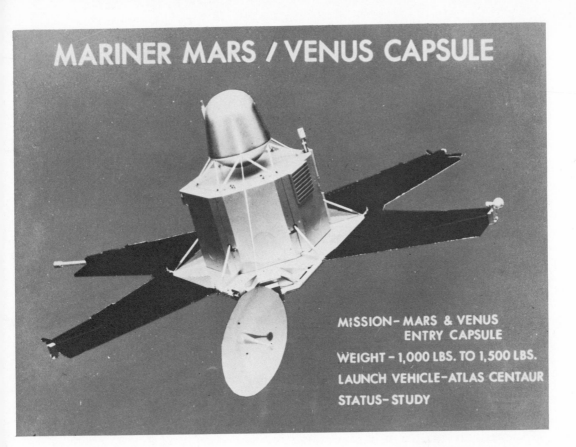

MARINER MARS / VENUS CAPSULE

MISSION – MARS & VENUS
ENTRY CAPSULE
WEIGHT – 1,000 LBS. TO 1,500 LBS.
LAUNCH VEHICLE – ATLAS CENTAUR
STATUS – STUDY

which had helped launch the era of space exploration, led the world's scientists to propose new efforts of this kind. After many meetings, it was decided to try next to make a massive assault on clarifying the many theories of space and the sun's activity—such as, sunspots and solar storms, which follow an eleven-year cycle. At a high point of this cycle, the sun is extremely active for a period of several years. Many sudden storms send out streams of plasma that disrupt radio and TV communications on earth. Then, as the cycle progresses, the number of storms subsides until finally a period arrives in which there are relatively few storms again, after which activity increases once more until it reaches a year of maximum activity. During 1964-1965 the sun's activity was at its lowest and this period was called the International Year of the Quiet Sun.

When the sun is seething most furiously and sending out its strongest destructive tongues of hot plasma, it is difficult if not impossible to differentiate among the types of charged particles it emits. But in quiet years, when activity on the sun's surface is low, sensitive instruments can register these changes more easily, even though the sun's surface is still dotted with a few violent solar storms.

By measuring the different effects of sunspot activity in a quiet year, scientists hope to figure out why the cycle works as it does. It is known, for instance, that particles from outside the solar system— from the cosmos—are constantly entering the magnetic field of the sun. The sun's emanations then interact with these cosmic particles and speed their course. Information on hand showed this interaction changes at the approach of a solar storm. If scientists could learn why these things happen, they could better understand why solar flares occur. Knowing this, they might then figure out ways of predicting well in advance just when solar flares would erupt.

Knowing when solar flares occur is vitally important to any manned space flight. An interplanetary weather-prediction system is definitely needed. If a human being is in outer space when a major flare starts up, no amount of shielding will save him from the searing energy of the storm. He would be dead in seconds.

Since Mariner C was to be in space in 1965, it was selected to carry a cosmic-ray sensor identical to those to be installed on several other spacecraft that would also be launched during this period. Scientists planned to launch one craft, the Pioneer (designed for NASA by Space Technology Laboratories), in an orbit moving from the earth toward the sun. Several months later another Pioneer was scheduled for launch in an outward orbit—toward Mars. (But both Pioneers would travel in orbits not too far from that of earth.)

With both Pioneers and the Mariner aloft, if a stream of plasma were to erupt from the sun and propel cosmic particles to faster and faster speeds, the particles would be measured in turn by each vehicle as they moved outward into deeper space. And if a beam of particles were to reach one spacecraft and not the others, scientists could find out from this how the solar magnetic field affects galactic fields. Mariner C would thus be able not only to give us some of the first

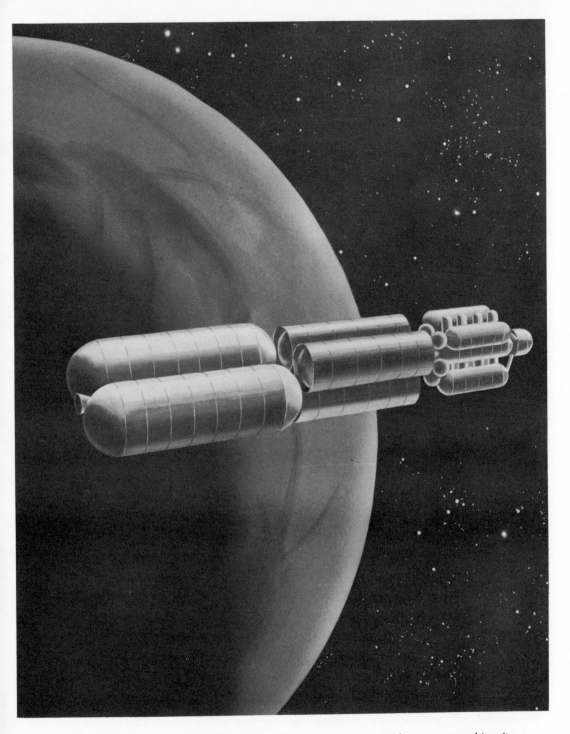

The time is the mid-1980s and a huge Mars convoy is shown approaching its destination . . .

substantial facts needed about Mars, it would also help form the weather-prediction system that would make manned missions to Mars much safer.

The design cycle went its way once more. Mariner C proceeded on rough mockup to system-test models. The information gained from previous years of space flights had led to the design of vastly improved test facilities. Once more, special structural-test and thermal-control models were built. In the Mariner II thermal-control tests, no large testing chamber was available to test the effects of sunlight in space on the craft. The engineers had had to simulate that space condition by placing small heaters on all exposed surfaces of the model. But as Mariner II was being built, a large solar-simulation chamber was being erected at JPL. Scientists counted on the information from the Venus flight to show if their design ideas for the chamber approximated the conditions of outer space. Fortunately, the Mariner II data showed that the approach taken was correct.

In the new test installation, special pumps removed all the air until an almost perfect vacuum remained inside the sealed room. Cold gas circulated in tubes around the room to freeze out any remaining gas particles and also to duplicate the intense cold of "black" space. At the same time, intense heat from a series of special lamps located in the top of the chamber simulated sunlight. The lamps could be adjusted to duplicate the higher heat load of the Venus trip or the lower heat load for Mars. A full-scale Mariner C went into this chamber after preliminary thermal-control tests with smaller models. The artificial sunlight beat down on one side of the model while, on the opposite surface, the cold of space was felt. Over the weeks of testing, the model was placed in different positions to simulate the earth-Mars trajectory. The sensitive instruments attached to the model sent out numerous readings. Scientists checked and rechecked this data to see if the thermal-control values for each part of the vehicle were right. Also, the electronic system in this and other test equipment could now be operated under conditions much closer to those of actual flight. With luck, the Mariner C mission would avoid some of the heart-stopping emergencies of Mariner II.

CHAPTER 15

THE MONTHS went by. The year 1963 turned into 1964 and once more the buildup began toward another Mariner mission. By mid-1964, the new Atlas D booster and the more powerful Agena D would be well along in production. By the beginning of summer, the completed spacecraft were undergoing system tests at JPL. By fall, the three Mariner Mars craft would be placed on the huge Air Force transport plane for shipment to the Atlantic Missile Range at Cape Kennedy. In October and November of 1964, combined tests of the complete launch system would begin.

The fears and tensions, the awareness that failures are always possible, remained as the hundreds of people involved in the program worked toward the launching goal. As the time came for the Mariner C countdown at Cape Kennedy, the NASA-JPL team knew chances for success were better than they had been two years before. And even if the mission failed—if the craft blew up on the launch pad or the signals faded as the ship moved outward toward Mars—the Mariner II had proven the job could be done. If the 1964 shots didn't work, then the experience gained would make it more likely that the 1966 or 1969 attempts would succeed.

Once past Mars, Mariner would send signals for only about twenty to forty days more before its electronic system would turn off. Then it would slip silently into an orbit around the sun. Looking beyond the Mariner program, however, NASA and JPL designers and scientists were already hard at work on the successor to Mariner. Called Project Voyager, it would mark a giant step beyond the first interplanetary series. Where the Mariner Mars probe would only go past Mars and scan it for twenty minutes, Voyager would go into orbit around the planet to join Mars' mysterious moons. Voyager vehicles were also planned to orbit Venus.

Project Voyager wasn't planned to begin until 1969 or 1970, after the Mariner project had fully run its course. It would include unmanned landing vehicles equipped to take direct TV pictures both while hovering above the planet's surface and while sitting on the surface itself. Special digging equipment would take samples of the soil, send it to a special chemical-analysis chamber, then radio back the makeup of the soil to earth receivers. This operation is also one of the major tasks of the Surveyor moon-landing probe. Just as the Surveyor information is important in order to design a manned landing craft for the Apollo moon program, Voyager information is the key to manned landings on Mars.

Though part of Voyager's purpose is to gain information for manned landings, it has another major scientific task to perform as well. In fact, most scientists would consider this its most important job. And this is to study both Mars and Venus in order to find any information about the origin and evolution of the solar system and of life within it. But because Venus' surface temperature is 800° F., the biological portion of the Voyager probes is consigned exclusively to Mars.

None of the boosters available in 1963 could send enough payload into space for the Voyager mission. But at the time there were systems in the process of development that ultimately could. The Centaur upper stage, which had not been ready for Mariner II by late 1963, was redesigned by NASA and General Dynamics/Astronautics for the Sur-

112

When the space vehicle approaches Mars, an excursion module, similar in appearance to this one, will carry astronauts down to the surface of Mars.

MARS VEHICLE - SPACE CONFIGURATION

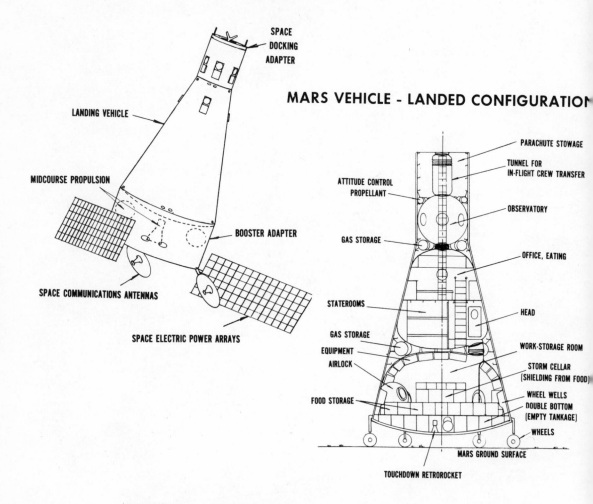

MARS VEHICLE - LANDED CONFIGURATION

SPACE DOCKING ADAPTER

LANDING VEHICLE

MIDCOURSE PROPULSION

BOOSTER ADAPTER

SPACE COMMUNICATIONS ANTENNAS

SPACE ELECTRIC POWER ARRAYS

PARACHUTE STOWAGE

TUNNEL FOR IN-FLIGHT CREW TRANSFER

ATTITUDE CONTROL PROPELLANT

OBSERVATORY

GAS STORAGE

OFFICE, EATING

STATEROOMS

HEAD

GAS STORAGE

WORK-STORAGE ROOM

EQUIPMENT AIRLOCK

STORM CELLAR (SHIELDING FROM FOOD)

WHEEL WELLS DOUBLE BOTTOM (EMPTY TANKAGE)

FOOD STORAGE

WHEELS

MARS GROUND SURFACE

TOUCHDOWN RETROROCKET

The final step—a step which may be closer than we think—is to send colonizing teams to Mars. A possible vehicle to carry men and equipment for such a mission is shown in these diagrams by engineer Chester Haig of McDonnell Aircraft Co.

veyor moon probe. By 1964-1965, Centaur would be playing a key part in the Apollo program as well. It was also being considered for later Mariner flights. On the Surveyor flight, Centaur would be launched by an Atlas vehicle. And though the Atlas does not have enough power for the Voyager mission, the Saturn IB booster developed for Apollo does. It was therefore decided that Voyager's need could be met by putting a Centaur or a similar high-energy upper stage on the Saturn. Studies indicated that by 1969 or 1970, a 2,000- to 3,000-pound Voyager, including a landing vehicle of about 1,000 pounds, could be sent to Mars or Venus.

After Voyager? NASA-sponsored studies are under way at many research laboratories. Similar experiments, paid for by aerospace companies themselves, are in preparation for the most exciting step of all: the eventual landing of men on the surface of Mars in the 1970's or 1980's. The most likely time for this seems to be in the 1980's. The mission could be accomplished in the 1970's, but it would entail too expensive a program to make the speedup in the space effort worthwhile. Even with the date as far away as the 1980's, though, plans have to be made now. The hundreds of studies on paper that eventually lead to the choice of a vehicle are an undertaking that dwarf even the Apollo moon program. Scientific and engineering conferences are held to compare plans for all types of strange-looking space vehicles. The pros and cons of different ways of doing the job continue to be discussed. But the way has been opened and it is no longer a question of whether man *can* land on another planet, but when he *will* be doing it. Someday, most scientists agree, colonies on Mars will be a reality.

The story of Mariner is not an end in itself. Each Mariner voyage rises to a peak of tension—as the mission goes on to success or failure. But each event in the program is merely one step in a long series. Together, these steps build the story of Mariner. Mariner, in turn, leads to Voyager, and finally come the first steps of man into the cosmos. Man can hardly begin to imagine the wonders that will be found on other worlds. One thing only is certain—the journey will be exciting and, eventually, rewarding for all mankind.

APPENDIX

MARINER DETAILS

LAUNCH VEHICLE Atlas-Agena B

DIMENSIONS, LAUNCH VEHICLE:

Total height, with Mariner spacecraft, plus shroud, 100 plus feet
Atlas, 66 feet
Agena B, 22 feet
Mariner with shroud, 12 feet

DIMENSION, MARINER:

In launch position, folded
Diameter, 5 feet
Height, 9 feet 11 inches
In cruise position, panels unfolded
Span, 16 feet 6 inches
Height, 11 feet 11 inches

WEIGHT, MARINER II:

Structure, 77 pounds
Solar Panels, 48 pounds
Electronics, 146 pounds
Propulsion, 32 pounds
Launch-Backup Battery, 33 pounds
Miscellaneous Equipment, 70 pounds
Scientific Experiments, 41 pounds

GROSS WEIGHT, 447 pounds

MARINER II SCIENTIFIC EXPERIMENTS

EXPERIMENTS	DESCRIPTION	EXPERIMENTERS
Microwave Radiometer	Determine the temperature of the planet surface and details concerning its atmosphere.	Dr. A. H. Barrett, Massachusetts Institute of Technology; D. E. Jones, JPL; Dr. J. Copeland, Army Ordnance Missile Command; Dr. A. E. Lilley, Harvard College Observatory.
Infrared Radiometer	Determine any fine structure of the cloud layer.	Dr. L. D. Kaplan, JPL and University of Nevada; Dr. G. Neugebauer, JPL; Dr. C. Sagan, University of California at Berkeley.
Magnetometer	Measure changes in the planetary and interplanetary magnetic fields.	P. J. Coleman, NASA; Dr. L. Davis, Caltech; Dr. E. J. Smith, JPL; Dr. C. P. Sonett, NASA.
Ion Chamber and Particle Flux Detector	Measure charged-particle intensity and distribution in interplanetary space and in the vicinity of the planet.	Dr. H. R. Anderson, JPL; Dr. H. V. Neher, Caltech; Dr. J. Van Allen, State University of Iowa.
Cosmic Dust Detector	Measure the density and direction of cosmic dust.	W. M. Alexander, NASA Goddard Space Flight Center.
Solar Plasma Spectrometer	Measure the intensity of low energy protons from the sun.	M. Neugebauer, and Dr. C. W. Snyder, JPL.

SOLAR GLOSSARY

Age: Estimated 10 billion years

Diameter: About 864,000 (109 times that of Earth).

Volume: 1,300,000 times that of Earth.

Density: 0.26

Mass: 333,000 × Earth

Distance from Earth: 93 million miles or 1 Astronomical Unit.

Specific Gravity: 1.41 (Earth, 5.52)

Surface Gravity: 28 (Earth, 1)

Velocity of Escape: 383 miles a second (Earth, 6.95 miles a second)

Surface Temperature: 10,300°F (Earth, average of 32°F)

Interior Temperature: 35 to 50 million degrees F (Earth, 5000°F)

Rotation: Varies, more rapid near the equator where average is 24.65 days.

Sun's Antapex: The point in space from which the sun is moving. (Generally believed to be the constellation of Columba.)

Photosphere: The visible disk of the sun, diameter ½°.

Chromosphere: The rosy red (light pinkish) layer, or atmosphere which extends out several thousand miles. Visible only during solar eclipse because it is overwhelmed by the photosphere's brilliance. Usually observed through a spectro-helioscope.

Corona: The sun's outermost layer visible only through a coronograph or total solar eclipse when it appears as a varying white halo against the dark silhouette of the moon. When there are relatively few sunspots, the corona has an almost smooth outline. During disturbances, however, its streamers can extend outward for millions of miles.

Prominences: Geysers of bright hydrogen that come up from the surface, or photosphere. Flame-like in appearance they sometimes shoot outward a million miles. The more spectacular seem to be associated with sunspots.

Spicules: The fine structure in the corona seen at the poles. Has lifetime measured in seconds.

Sunspots: The dark areas in the photosphere having extremely strong magnetic fields. Apparently they are the venting valve for the tremendous forces at work below the photosphere. Some of the larger ones have a total area of several million miles. Temperature within a sunspot is believed to be several thousand degrees less than that at the surface. The number of sunspots varies over a solar cycle of 11.3 years between maximum and minimum sunspot activity.

Gauss: A measurement of the strength of a magnetic field. The magnetic field of sunspots sometimes reaches 3,000 gauss.

Flocculi: The bright or dark calcium clouds that are found near sunspots. Sometimes called plages. The general form for any chromospheric turbine.

Granulations: Usually elliptical in shape and resembling grains of rice, they appear over the entire surface of the sun. Constantly in motion, they have a turbulent life of only a few minutes before they die and are replaced by new granules.

Limb: The edge of the sun's disk, darker than the center of the disk.

Gegenschein: The counter glow or faint reflection of sunlight from dust-size meteoroids in space.

Cosmic Ray Particles: Mostly protons with energies ranging from less than 10 MEV (million electron volts) to 50 BEV (billion electron volts).

Umbra: The dark central portion of a sunspot.

Penumbra:	The grayish-filament-like structures surrounding the umbra.
Solar Constant:	A figure which represents the rate of energy received from the sun. Figured as the amount of energy received on the surface of a hypothetical sphere outside the earth's atmosphere. Solar constant is 1.94 calories per square centimeter.
Cosmic Year:	The period of time, about 200 million Earth years, required for the sun to be carried completely around the center of the Milky Way galaxy by the rotation of the galaxy. Our sun is just now reaching voting age of 21 cosmic years.
Carbon Cycle:	A process which produces the energy in stars, in which millions of tons of hydrogen are transformed into millions of tons of helium with only a few million tons converted into energy.
Proton-Proton Cycle:	The process of creating stellar energy at a lower temperature than that required for the carbon cycle. Probably the most important energy source in the sun.
Gamma Ray:	A quantum of electromagnetic radiation emitted by a nucleus as a result of a quantum transition between two energy levels of the nucleus. Energies range from 100,000 to 1 million electron volts.
Ultraviolet:	A range of radiation of frequencies next higher than those of visible light.
Spectrometer:	An instrument which measures intensity in various wave lengths. A dispersing element such as a diffraction-grating is employed to give the various wave lengths.

MECHANICAL PROPERTIES OF MARS

	Miles
Distance from Sun	
mean	141,500,000
aphelion	154,100,000
perihelion	128,000,000

Distance from the Earth	
perihelion opposition	34,800,000
aphelion opposition	61,500,000
aphelion conjunction	240,000,000

Orbital velocity, miles/second	
mean	14.98
at aphelion	13.64
at perihelion	16.45

Escape velocity, per second (parabolic)	3.13
Circular velocity at surface, per second	2.21
Equatorial diameter	4220

Length of day	
sidereal	24h, 37m, 22.668s
solar	24h, 39m, 35.247s

Length of year		868.979 earth days
Mass	(Earth = 1)	0.108
Volume	(Earth = 1)	0.151
Density	(Earth = 1)	0.710
Density	(Water = 1)	4.0 ± 0.1
Surface area	(Earth = 1)	0.278
Gravity, surface	(Earth = 1)	0.38
Eccentricity		0.0934

ESTIMATES OF RUSSIAN SPACE BOOSTERS

Vehicle	Launch Date	Payload (pounds)	Launch Weight (pounds)	Number of 1st Stage Engines	First Stage Thrust (pounds)
Sputnik 1	1957	184	314,000	2	440,000
Sputnik 2	1957	1,120	314,000	2	440,000
Sputnik 3	1958	2,925	325,000	2	440,000
Sputniks 4-6	1960	10,000	650,000	4	880,000
Sputniks 7-8	1961	14,292	630,000	4	880,000
Sputniks 9-10	1961	10,400	650,000	4	880,000
Vostoks 1-2	1961	10,400	650,000	4	880,000
Advanced four engine booster*		40-55,000	1,250,000+	4	1,760,000 to 2,000,000
Advanced six engine booster**		80-105,000	1,950,000 to 2,140,000	6	2,640,000 to 3,000,000

* Basic engine tested in late 1950s. Booster system probably ready for operation in mid 1960s. This performance is in line with that of the United States Saturn Apollo booster which is due to be in operation in the late 1960s.

** Advanced version of the above four engine design using two more engines in the first stage. Operational in the late 1960s.

TABLE OF SOLAR SYSTEM

	Sun	Moon	Mercury	Venus	Earth	Mars	Jupiter	Saturn	Uranus	Neptune	Pluto
Diameter (miles)	870,000	2,170	3,100	7,750	7,970	4,140	87,300	71,000	32,000	31,000	3,700
Mean Distance From Sun (millions of miles)	—	—	36	67	93	142	484	887	1,785	2,800	3,675
Escape Velocity (miles per second)	387	1.5	2.6	6.4	7	4	37	22	13	14	?
Surface Gravity (Earth = 1)	28	.16	.36	.86	1	.40	2.64	1.17	.91	1.12	?
Eccentricity of Orbit (circle = 0)	—	.054	.206	.007	.017	.093	.048	.056	.047	.009	.248
Inclination to Ecliptic (degrees)	—	5.8	7	3.2	—	1.5	1.18	2.3	.46	1.46	17.8
Number of Satellites	—	—	0	0	1	2	12	9	5	2	0
Period of Revolution	—	27.3 days	88 days	224 days	365 days	1.9 years	11.9 years	29.4 years	84 years	164.8 years	247.7 years

INDEX

The Authors

Irwin Stambler is engineering editor of *Space/Aeronautics* magazine, where he has overall responsibility for articles on aircraft design, materials, aerodynamics, spacecraft design, missile design and production methods. He has an M.S. in aeronautical engineering from New York University and has studied in other fields of engineering at three other universities. As an aviation engineer, he has worked for Republic Aviation and Chase Aircraft. Recognized as an authoritative writer on space programs, his work has appeared in a half dozen national magazines. Mr. Stambler has written several books including *Space Ship: The Story of the X-15, Find a Career in Aviation, The Wonders of Underwater Exploration,* and *Project Gemini.*

He lives with his wife and four children in Beverly Hills, California.

Gordon Ashmead is head of technical and manufacturing projects in the public relations division of the Douglas Aircraft Company. He has been a writer for over thirty years, and has served as editor on a number of architectural, machinery and technical magazines. He has published over 2,000 technical, and many nontechnical, articles on such diverse subjects as architecture, decorating, medicine and furniture. He has co-authored, with Irwin Stambler, *Find a Career in Engineering.* Mr. Ashmead and his wife live in Pacific Palisades, California.